Nine

Pat Warner

By the same Author:
Lock Keeper's Daughter

Nine Nightingales

Pat Warner

Brewin Books

First published October 1997

by Brewin Books, Studley, Warwickshire.

ISBN 1 85858 103 6

British Library Cataloguing in Publication Data

A Catalogue record for this book is available

from the British Library

Typeset in Garamond Book

and made and printed by

Heron Press, Kings Norton, Birmingham

To
My family and their families
Hoping that their world will be a peaceful one

Contents

Acknowledgements

The Author wishes to thank................

The Rev. D. Copley former vicar of Tardebigge
Staff of the Redditch Library
The lads of Tardebigge Village
The late Frank Colledge and the late Herbert Jones
Maurice Clarke Antiques & Alan Foxall - Redditch Pictorial History
Society for the loan of photographs and items relating to Hewell.
John Emms, Miss Margeret Beake, Mr. Maurice Griffin.
Miss Gertrude Beszant
Maire and Robin from Kidderminster who kindly brought along the
V. A. D. Hospital photographs of nurses and patients sent by
Mrs Harvey of Wychbold near Droitwich.
Mike Johnson for his video "Hewell Remembered"
District Nurse colleague Caroline Hirons for the loan of the diary
relating to the Tardebigge Nursing Association.
Mr. R Mayneord.
Janette Hill for her drawings and wild flowers.
Peter Hill Photography
David Hill Drawings
The Author's husband for his assistance with maps and Karen and Julian
for the many hours spent putting typing on to a word processor.

This book is not intended to be a technical history about Hewell Estate and the village hall.

It is meant to convey to the reader how a little girl, a lock keeper's daughter, became enchanted with a hall and it's history and a family which have since become a part of the bygone days of Tardebigge.

It was the many stories told by her father of the First World War, the use of the Village hall as a hospital and her love and fascination for a treasured collection of illustrated coloured song cards published by Bamford & Co. England and New York and the many songs which the troops sang as they marched or sailed away to some foreign land.

The Author was also allowed a weekly copy of the "Childrens Newspaper" edited by Arthur Mee originally to be called "The Little Paper".

The first edition published on March 22nd 1919 cost 1 1/2d. It told the story of the world today for the men and women of tomorrow. It was read and understood by all members of the family and the last edition was on May 1st 1965.

How sad!!!

It was the pictures and stories of the wounded troops, the Red Cross and the V.A.D. (Voluntary Aid Detachment) Nurses, which played a large part in a determination to follow a career in the nursing profession which lasted 55 years.

The loss to the parishoners of the Hewell Estate which occurred with the death of the 2nd Earl of Plymouth in 1943 was a very sad occasion, parishoners were no longer free to wander the park or use the amenities such as the village hall which had been the means of happy hours for so many people.

This hall was given to the local people by the 1st Earl of Plymouth and throughout my childhood I was fascinated by the bas reliefs, dedicated to Clive of India, that adorned the walls just inside the doors of the Great Hall. I have always felt that these beautiful tributes should be included in a story about Tardebigge. Indeed even to this day I have discovered that many people did not know of their existence.

It was my family that encouraged me to write this story as a record of days now past.

This is a record of a way of life that can never be repeated.

Introduction

All the postcards shown in this book are from the author's private collection.

All stories relating to incidents which occurred during the First World War are taken from conversations and notes made during the author's fifty five years of nursing.

Also many of the stories were related to her by her father.

Many of the stories told to her by retired First World War veterans were repetitive, which makes them unforgettable.

Many of the men were blind and limbless, especially the ones that she met many years ago at St. Dunstans, Rottingdean, Sussex, these men were anxious for a good listener.

Family relations were keen to tell of sights and sounds they had encountered, comrades never forgotten from long ago.

Men from "Toc H", a club or society formed after the First World War for christian comradeship. T.H. was a telegraphic code, initials of Talbot House, Poperinghe, Belgium. original headquarters.

Maps and Cards

Map of the Hewell Estate and programme of sale.

Map of the Lickey Hills.

1914 -1918 Coloured christmas and birthday cards.

1914 - 1918 Souvenir cards of Germany.

1914 - 1918 Souvenir cards of France.

1914 - 1918 Humorous cards.

Photographs

Hewell Grange members of the Plymouth family.

Lickey Monument.

Worcestershire Yeomanry billeted in Hewell Park.

Soldiers & Nurses inside and outside the village Hall and V.A. D. hospital

Hewell Lake - Tardebigge reservoir - Drawings and wild flowers
drawn by Jeanette Hill.

Poems, Verses, Victorian Ballads.

SWEET NIGHTINGALE

My Sweetheart, come along,
Don't you hear the sweet song,
The sweet notes of the nightingale flow?
Don't you hear the fond tale
Of the sweet nightingale
As she sings in the valley below,
As she sings in the valley below.

Pray sit yourself down
With me on the ground
On this bank where the primroses grow,
You shall hear the fond tale
Of the sweet nightingale,
As she sings in the valley below,
As she sings in the valley below.

Part of the song which I learnt at Tardebigge school during the
1930's.

CHAPTER ONE

First Impressions

I stood and gazed at the "pictures" on the wall, and once again I was transported into a little world of my own & brought back to reality by my father's voice telling me not to stand there day dreaming.

This was my first visit to Tardebigge village hall, quite an occasion when one is not quite five years of age.

We has walked from the Reservoir at Tardebigge because my father had to "see a man about a dog", this was his way of telling me not to ask any questions as to why we were about to embark on this great journey, "In any case Pat you may as well get used to long walks, you'll be walking this way to school and back every day for a long time".

"Anyway", continued father, "we may as well take a look at this hall that the Earl of Plymouth has been good enough to provide for the parishioners, we must be courteous and pay our respects".

My father always believed that one should DO THINGS the proper way and so there was I, a lock keepers daughter gazing at the most beautiful "pictures" that I has ever seen.

What ever are they, I asked myself, I haven't seen anything like this in the

My house by Tardebigge Reservoir. A Selection of the wild flower which grew on the Reservoir Bank Engine House Chimney is shown in the Background. It was classed as a landmark - Demolished 1939.

churchyard when I go to see my mother's grave, perhaps they are something to do with the Dicken's stories which father reads to me at night. Suddenly it dawned on me just what these "pictures" were "I know what these are", I shouted "it's a Peep Behind the Scenes", this was always my favourite story about a little girl called Rosalie who lived in a caravan on a fair ground, it was a very sad story and to my tiny mind these pictures on the wall also told a very sad story.

Suddenly a voice behind me said "Are you still gazing at those statues our Pat, you"ll be dreaming about them tonight, wait until you get to school, no doubt you'll learn all about them, some dim and distant relation of Plymouth family he is, not for you to worry about, you'll be coming here when your older to be taught cookery and laundry, you might even be in a school play or something like that and be up on that stage there, you never can tell, anyhow it's time we made tracks for home, it's a long way home and it's beginning to get dusk".

As I wandered along the canal side holding on to my fathers hand and dawdling as usual I was hoping that if we didn't get home before it was dark the Parish Lamp (the moon) would shine down and cast weird shadows across the cut (the canal), we might even hear the sounds of Black Bess's hooves as she thundered along the old London Road past the Engine House, legends tell us that this was the way which Dick Turpin rode from York.

"You are very quiet for once" remarked father, "suppose you are still thinking about them "pictures ", don't you get worrin your pretty little head about them things, you'll find out about them soon enough anyway I'm glad I've been an' taken a look at that hall, in a small village like this we're very fortunate to have such a magnificent building".

Tardebigge Reservoir 1896 - Grandad Warner

A ride on a sledge with Father 1927.

The village hall, by this time had been open for 18 years and was already steeped in history, used as a hospital during the Great War 1914 - 1918 my father reminded me that if it hadn't been for those boys in blue we may not be here to tell the tale. "You just think about those wounded, those boys in blue, walking in the park, enjoying the fresh air, away from their loved ones but also from the mud and the noise of the trenches".

I thought for a moment and remembered my precious Great War song cards, sets of illustrated coloured cards, each one printed with the verse of songs which were popular during that era with a different colour picture for each verse, published by Bamford & Co. England and New York.

"But father , the soldiers on my cards are in brown not blue and they have bandages on their legs".

"My dear lassie, those are puttees not bandages and their uniform is khaki, Blue is a colour they wear when they are allowed out of the hospital grounds, that is so that people will recognise, them".

Still deep in thought I wondered, dare I ask him what puttees are? He always tells me if you don't ask you'll never know!!

A puttee is a long strip of cloth wound around the leg like bandage, it serves as a gaiter (which is usually leather) fitting from below the knee to the ankle, now don't you go and ask what gaiters are because you already know, don't you?

Oh Yes, I know what gaiters are, those dreadful things I have to wear when it's cold with hundreds of buttons up each side, I have to do them up with a button hook.

"Yes", father went on, "you are a very lucky lass to have leather ones, they cost a lot of money, I'll bet there are not many lock keepers daughters that have any at all, let alone leather ones".

Oh yes, maybe I was lucky and also lucky enough to fully understand exactly just what puttees were.............

"Come along now Pat put you best leg forward, it's a long walk back to the reservoir and your sister will think we'll have fallen in the cut".

Wandering along the towpath and still deep in thought I was trying to figure out why I was lucky, my mother had died just after my third birthday and my sister Isobel had come home to keep house.

My love and fascination for the canals began at the early age of three when I was lulled to sleep by the waves which lapped against the walls of the lock outside our house, if the night was rough and stormy I could also hear the waves from the reservoir which lashed against the wall at the back of our house.

I lay in bed thinking the Gods of Valhalla are very angry tonight.

My world consisted of sunshine in summer, snow in winter, the call of the birds in the spring and the beautiful hues of autumn, a world of happy and leisurely days, very poor we were but very contented. A ride on a canal barge was a great treat, the heavy horses, the donkeys and all the wild animals were my friends, I was free and also very safe to wander anywhere.

Tardebigge Reservoir, A big freeze up - 1927

Walks in Hewell Park collecting chestnuts to roast on an open fire all added to the excitement of the long winter evenings.

Childhood days in Tardebigge were happy and peaceful days, days full of stories, legends about the Gods of Valhalla, Odin and Thor , Brunhild and Seigfried, tales of the Norsemen.

Freedom to wander the fields and lanes without a care, money never seemed to play a part because we hadn't any. If we had a penny we didn't waste it on bus fares, a penny (old money) could be put to much better use .... so we walked.

Soon I would be starting school so I would have to get used to walking .... up and down the canal side twice a day................ With or without my leggings ...Ah ... but they were no longer leggings they were my Puttees, I'm quite sure I could have put khaki bandages on much, much quicker.

I couldn't know then what a large part of my future life would revolve around the Village Hall.

I'm always very glad that I listened to my father's little ditties, he always had so many stories to tell, he had left school at the age of 12 to walk nine miles to work and nine miles back. His school days consisted of the three "R's"

Tardebigge Reservoir, The Drought - 1930

13

but he could read and write extremely well for the education he had received. Indeed, I learned my first nursery rhyme long before I started school.

"Mrs Bond", from the Childrens Song Book published before 1900 and was also known as "The Baby's Opera".

What have you got for dinner, Mrs. Bond?

There's beef in the larder and ducks in the pond.

Chorus - Dilly, Dilly, Dilly come and be killed for you must be stuffed and customers filled.

Pray send us first the beef Mrs. Bond, then we'll have the ducks that are swimming in the pond.

Chorus - I have been to the ducks that are swimming in the pond, but I can't fetch them in to be killed Mrs. Bond.

Chorus - Mrs. Bond, she went down to the pond in a rage with her apron full of onions and sage crying,

You ungrateful little ducks don't I feed you every day?

Oh yes Mrs. Bond but we would rather fly away.

Quack, Quack, Quack Goodbye Mrs. Bond

Flap, Flap, Flap. Goodbye Mrs. Bond.

My father was a good teacher, very patient, looking back I cannot remember a time when I could not read.

One of the questions he asked me was from a poem written long before I was born was about a teacher who set her class a simple sum.

"If there were nine sheep in a field and one went into the next field how many would be left behind"?

Then up spoke young Mary

A farmers daughter she

And not as good at figures

As she had ought to be

"Well"? said the teacher

"Come, tell us if you know".

"Please Miss, if one went out

All the rest would go!....................

I often think that in many ways I was reared on First World War songs, my father never said he would put some coal on the fire it was always "Keep the Home Fires Burning". When I packed my suitcase to stay with my aunt and uncle, the Wattons at Diglis Lock, Worcester he would say, "Well, have you packed up your troubles in your old kit bag".

Often when we had a long walk ahead he would say "Come on lassie put

The Vicarage, Tardebigge

your best foot forward, there's a long, long trail a winding unto the land of my dreams. Where the nightingales are singing and the white moon beams". By the time we arrived home the moon would be shining it would be passed 6 o'clock near to my bedtime, my first visit would be up the garden path to the little wooden hut "the privy", unless I was disturbed I would be quite happy to sit on this little wooden seat "until the cows came home". (Old country saying).

But the night was still and the water on the reservoir was calm, what I was really waiting for was the song of the Nightingale to come drifting across the water, those lovely musical notes "hu-eet, hu-eet"
loud and forgettable. I had heard them many times before but I know I would never be lucky enough to see this beautiful bird.

"Come along Pat, don't sit there dreaming all night".

"Well", said Isobel "You're very late where have you been?

"We've been talking to the Earl of Plymouth, down by the lake in Hewell Park, he was listening for the Nightingale".

"You're a fibber our Pat, the Earl wouldn't waste his time".

"She's right" said father"The Earl is very interested in nature and there are lots of wild flowers by the lake, we also went to take a look at the village hall".

At this point I chirped in "Yes it has a lovely picture on the wall and one day I will write a story about them".

"In your dreams" said father "Now get to bed and don't tell any more fibs. (lies). I can never remember hearing anyone called a liar.

Those tall brass shell cases which stood in our hearth, they could have told many war stories, standing upright in the hearth, the glow from the fire casting strange shadows on the polished brass which was so bright it could be a mirror. I often used to sit and gaze at them wondering which part of the world they had come from, how much destruction they had caused. If only they could talk and tell me about their adventures...............if only..........

I have often wished that I had known the Earl of Plymouth that my father knew, sadly he died in 1923 the year before I was born.

The young Earl, Ivor Miles, who succeeded his father, we often met in the park walking around with his children who were riding their ponies. Like his father, he too was interested in Flora and Fauna and liked to watch birds around Hewell Lake.

Along with the other children from Tardebigge school I would see the new Earl and his family many times at church functions, Christmas parties at Hewell Grange, Strawberry teas and fetes and school plays which would be held in the park weather permitting or in the Village Hall during the winter months.

Ghostly echoes from the past
Are fresh within my mind.
A rugged face, a friendly word,
A happy soul, so kind......
A child's swing on an apple tree,
A nightingale sings so sweet,
So many memories of yester years
Which make my life complete......
A soft summer breeze, a walk in the woods,
A seat beneath an oak,
All these memories so very dear
Still remind me of gentle folk.....

(Written by the Author)

St Bartholomew's Church and School at Tardebigge stand majestically upon a hill overlooking the most magnificent views. Since 1777 Hiorn's tower one hundred and thirty five feet high has stood on Church Hill like a sentinel, lonely, watching and waiting. A silhouette to every passing stranger,

Lord of all it surveys.
A Norman church existing on this same site in 1138. Like any old church it is steeped in history.
The church bells rang out loud and clear every 5th of November to remind the parishioners of the failure of the Gunpowder Plot...
Chantry's White Marble Memorial. Tardebigge Church.
The monument hangs above the choir stalls on the East Wall. The inscription reads.....
Near this place are deposited the remains of the Other Archer (named after Othere the Norse King), Earl of Plymouth who lived in the year of our Lord 1833 terminated a life of fourty four years during which he had humbly but sincerely attempted to do his duty towards God and towards his neighbours.
"Enter not into judgement with thy servant O Lord".

St Bartholomew's Church and School at Tardebigge

The above inscription was found in his own handwriting a few hours after his death.
The monument was erected by Mary his widow and was placed on the East Wall of the knave, it was later removed to the chancel for the War Memorial to be put in it's place.
When this Earl died in 1833 and was buried at Tardebigge a huge crowd of people attended his funeral, included were all the soldiers of the Worcestershire Yeomanry, a very impressive sight as many of the Yeomanry were on horseback, this story was related to me by a native of the parish whose grandfather had been present.
Strange to think back to my early school years and to remember how spellbound I was as I listened to my teacher as she told us the stories about the Norsemen, the Viking Chiefs and the Gods of Vallhala, Odin and Thor, how instead of being buried they were pushed out to sea on a burning ship while the beautiful Brunhild wept as she watched her beloved engulfed in flames, slowly vanishing beyond the horizon.

Tardebigge Church & School Banner

East Window, Tardebigge Church. Designed by the Earl of Plymouth

How I loved those stories, I was completely carried away, my mind wandered off and very soon I was laid out in a flowering white robe, surrounded by huge white lilies, my arms folded across my chest, four strong fair haired Vikings gently carried me as I was carefully laid to rest on the top of a coal barge cabin.

Not a sound to be heard, no voices or sobbing, only the soft breeze as it gently moved the hem of my gossamer gown.

Suddenly a Viking Chief appeared brandishing a fiery torch and a ring of flames danced all around me and away across the cut I sailed.

My sister would stand and weep and she would call "Come back our Pat, I promise that you will never have to wash up again and you can sit on the closet seat all night if you want to".

Now the voice can scarcely be heard and I am going........going......thud.....I must have hit a rock, I hear a voice calling ......calling "For heavens sake Pat Warner do wake up. I've had to bang on the desk to make you realize that you're still in the classroom. You're either day dreaming or gazing through the windows at funerals. You must stay in after school and write down one hundred times, I must pay attention more attention, we'll see if that will bring you back to reality".

"Please Miss, I have to fetch the milk".

"Well, you will still have time".

"But it will be dark when I get home".

"That's your fault".

"My father will come and see you tomorrow if he hasn't any milk for his tea".

"Be quiet child ......".

Silly old thing why didn't she tell us that Lord Plymouth's ancestors were Vikings, bet she didn't know, well, maybe there's a little drop of Viking blood hidden away in me somewhere, who knows?...

The quiet towpaths of the canals have showered their peace and tranquillity over many a rambler, people resting awhile to watch the fish leaping out of the water and the moorhens gliding silently along the side of the canal bank.

Often there was nothing very special to watch so a visitor would just sit and relax and become lost in thought just for pleasure, the pressures of the week seemed many miles away.

Yet even the canals have many tales to tell, one which stands out in my mind was told to me by my father, it occurred on September 9th 1899.

It was in the early hours of that fateful day at Dudley Port next to the Stour Valley Brickworks that a 100 yard breach suddenly opened up in the canal towpath.

Water from two miles of the canal gushed into the 300 ft marlhole which supplied the brickworks with clay, this marlhole which had a surface boundary of three acres was completely flooded as was two acres of surrounding fields.

The water in the canal six miles away was so low that they were completely impassable.

Two boats nearby were caught in this tidal wave, one boatman hitched himself, his boat and his horse to the nearest telegraph pole and hung on, the other boatman lost his boat but managed to save himself and his horse by cutting his towrope.

Many telegraph poles were swept away and communications between Dudley and Birmingham were cut off.

The course of the canal covered a large proportion of the Hewell Estate. Before and after 1876 Lord Windsor was a big shareholder so the land was never sold to the canal company.

Lord Windsor wished to keep the estate intact just in case the canal project should be abandoned. It was Lord Windsor who was responsible for the first steam tugs to replace the "legers". These were a band of men who specialised in assisting to move the loaded boats through the tunnels. Lying on their backs on top of the cabins with their feet on the roof of the tunnel they would "walk" their way through.

A band of men waited at different ends of the tunnels with the intention of being employed by the "skipper of the boat". It was recorded that the "legers" spent many hours in Plymouth Arms and drank so much cider and home brewed ale that they were unable to concentrate on their work.

Many of the legers were drowned in Tardebigge Tunnel and it was for this reason that the Earl of Plymouth closed the licence of the Plymouth Arms and other local inns.

To me there has always been a tremendous bond between the Hewell Estate and the Tardebigge people.

So many, many memories for ......So many, many people............

Tardebigge School was part of the Hewell Estate, adjacent to the church which towered above the canal.

Hewell Park and it's surroundings held a fascination for me and the annual Christmas Party for all the Tardebigge school children was just like a fairy tale.

It was during my walks to school with my father that he would often tell me about the Great War song cards.

Poor father, no wonder he sounded weary, the number of times I had told him I would write a book, or a story....perhaps just a little one, just a tiny one.....

There were many other interesting things to be seen at Hewell. A beautiful herd of dairy cows wandering freely in a large field. A Victorian garden with a long wall surrounding it, peaches, vines, apricots growing in abundance.

A kitchen Garden wafted it's perfume of beautiful herbs, the rose garden filled the evening air with an undescribable lingering smell.

French and Italian garden fountains. Terraced grass steps leading up to the Water Tower built in 1901 - 1902.

Then of course there was that wonderful maze, a place where all the school children could hide and often become very, very lost.

The Water Tower was used to power the lifts in the Grange and also to work the fountains in the gardens.

The pond on the opposite side of the road a short distance away from the tower supplied the water.

A small wooden shed, which was situated near the edge of the lake in the park, housed the stopcock and pipes which released the water. This small pumping station with it's dull thumping sound was commonly known as "The Ram".

It was many years later on my numerous visits to the village hall that I remembered my father's words.

I was given a part to play in the Pantomimes and other functions held there. Every Friday we attended for cookery and laundry lessons. This was my golden opportunity to stand and gaze at "my lovely pictures" (the Bas reliefs). I was now more determined that ever to find out more about them. I didn't need a "Chocolate Soldier" for a hero, I had Clive of India, what more could a young lass wish for but it was many years later before I was able to delve into the true meaning of these "Pictures" which haunted my young life.

Hewell Water Tower

CHAPTER TWO

Hewell. Robert George Earl of Plymouth
1857 - 1923

HEWELL GRANGE

Situated halfway between Redditch and Bromsgrove in the heart of the
Worcestershire country side. The home of Robert George, Earl of Plymouth,
Lady Plymouth and their family from the year 1891. Also known as the
Windor's family home.

Tardebigge Village hall, situated on the main Redditch to Bromsgrove road
opposite the main lodge house leading into Hewell Park approx. 1/4 mile
away from Hewell Grange.

A gift from the Earl of Plymouth in 1911.

Many of the roads in Redditch owe their names to Hewell and the Windsor
family.

Hewell Road
Windsor Road
Plymouth Road
Clive Road
Oakley Road
Archer Road
Ivor Road
Grange Road
Lady Harriet's Lane.
Other Road

The present Hewell Grange which I knew and loved was built in 1885 -
1891.

The stone came from the Runcorn Quarries in Cheshire, brought down by
canal to within a mile or so from the house, carried on a tramway drawn by
horses up to the site in large blocks, cut up and worked upon the spot. The
site which was chosen for the new house was known as the "American
Garden". This time the house was situated a safe distance away from the
lake.

From the start the house was electrically wired, it was also centrally heated
in a primitive sense, known as the "Plenum System" for the movement of air.
Fresh air was drawn in through vents in the walls and convected into the

boiler - room, coal was very cheap in those days, the warm air was then circulated around the house and released into the rooms by the means of long narrow grills which lay along the top of the pannelling, the air eventually escaped through the large copper dome set in the roof. This dome was 12 foot in diameter and was fitted with copper pipes.

The tapestries, which held a great fascination for me, covered the walls of the great hall, well, to me they looked like enormous pictures, how was I to know that they were copies of the "Bussac Tapestries" which hang in the Cluny Museum in Paris.

One little point of interest is that little teak staircase in the offices going up to the bathroom and bedroom passage came from Lord Clive's house in India.

The Earl of Plymouth states in his book of Hewell that it would be a pity for further generations not to know these points of interest. Also the pieces of furniture that came from the Hewell workshop were made by A. Westover and A. Gwynne.

Lady Plymouth's sitting room ceiling shows a complete layout of the Maze coloured in gold and blue in Italian style. Silk used in the sitting room was woven at Hewell. Some of the floors were made out of oak cut in the park. The chapel is very beautiful, the woodwork ceiling which is hand carved is a copy of one in the Accademia in Venice.

There is marble frieze below the ceiling depicting cherubic faces each one

The Fountain Hewell

23

Hewell Grange - The stone door

with a different expression.

The stained glass windows are also very beautiful, one shows the Presentation of the Charter of Bordesley Abbey Land, another is St George and the Dragon.

Visits to Hewell Grange by my father were frequent, he was employed as a lock keeper at Tardebigge in 1909.

The land and trees around Tardebigge reservoir, where we lived, belonged to the Hewell Estate.

My father always spoke of the Earl with great admiration, during the potato famine in 1917 it was the Earl who gave instructions that the potatoes be reserved for the less well to do who could not afford any substitutes.

Extract from Robert George - Earl of Plymouth 1857 - 1923. (Privately Printed)

Among the many tributes paid to this noble man was the following.........

The Birmingham Daily Mail - March 10th 1923.

Among the most notable of the many public services performed by the late Earl of Plymouth was his generous and successful effort to save the Crystal Palace a national possession.

Birmingham produced both iron work and glasswork for this great and unique building which housed the International Exhibition of 1851 and attracted the largest cosmopolitan crowd that had ever been seen in London.

The manufacture by Messrs Chance of sixteen acres of glass which the building contained was an industrial feat unexampled in history.

It was through Lord Plymouth's generosity and his gift of £210,000 that it was saved for the nation.

The Earl was well loved by all, but the most moving words were from the Gardener's Chronicle March 17th 1923. Following his death.

The following words were written by James J. Graham, gardener at Hewell for seven years.

"I leave Hewell with a heavy heart knowing, that in leaving Lord and Lady Plymouth (Lady Phyllis) I am parting with employers much above the average in their consideration for others".

How memorable were Lord Plymouth's words......

"What ever changes may have come to us in life no one can erase the happy memories of the past. I shall not look upon his like again".

Many people had happy recollections of employment at Hewell so it was in the latter part of the 1980's while working as a practice nurse for the local doctor that I came into contact with a local patient Mike Johnson who was very interested in making video's of local interest on "Times Past", it was through my previous book "Lock Keeper's Daughter" that he discovered how well I knew Tardebigge and mentioned that he would like to make a video of Hewell Grange but, he added "I don't know anyone who lives in the area at all".

"Well", I replied "everyone knows who I am", so we set out, every spare

Hewell - The Lodge

evening we could and the result was "Hewell Remembered"................

Ext: From Interviews on Video "Hewell Remembered"

There were memories of the Shah of Persia's visit in July 1889. Also Princess Victoria (who later became Queen Victoria) of hunt balls and house parties. The late Frank College recalls his introduction to service at Hewell Grange, he was a young lad and not very happy to do a girl's job. He describes the walk from the main road down through the park as the longest and loneliest walk of his life. As he came into sight of the hugh arch door his heart sank. He entered through a small wicket door into a large covered courtyard and there, towering above him in a large black dress and white starched apron stood the formidable figure of Mrs. Gates the housekeeper. Employed as a Hall Boy he would live in, rise at 5.45 am. to open the side door for the cellar man.

Clean up and lay the fireplaces in the servants hall and stewards room and black lead the grates, lay the table and carry the food into the servants hall. There were three grooms, three footmen, five housemaids, one chauffeur plus visiting footmen and housemaids who accompanied visiting house parties. There were also one hundred bedrooms......... He would keep to a strict discipline and at all times he would be frequently remainded to "know his place".

Each morning he would walk up the park to the Village Hall and wait for the nine o'clock bus from Redditch to collect a large delivery of newspapers.

HEWELL GRANGE *The Seat of the Right Honourable Baron Windsor of Stanwell. Erected in the years 1884 to 1891*

He would then put on a green baize apron and clean the silver. He was paid 6/- weekly (old money) plus his keep.

The late Syd Wall also recalls the Redditch Brass Band playing at functions held in the park or at the grange. Hewell had it's own cricket team, a bowling green, county standard, all situated at the back of the Village Hall, sad to say the tennis court now lies under the Bromsgrove Highway.

At one period in time Royal Tennis was played at Hewell, this was also played in the days of Henry VIII. It was played in the same style and method as we now know badminton so it required an indoor court. Local folk lore has told me that on more than one occasion that the only product which could be used to stain the floor was ox blood!

The young man who was given this task said it was many days before he could enjoy a meal !!!!

The late Netta Bate (Mrs. Frisby, also my cookery mistress at the village hall) also had a tale to tell when she recalled the Hewell Fire Brigade, a strong young body of men from the village, how smart they looked in their brass hats and long black boots.

A huge outdoor bell was ready to summon the men who attended for regular fire drill.

Tardebigge V.A.D. Hospital 1914-1918, The Village Hall.
A gift from Lord Plymouth - 1911.

Card issued by John Player & Sons - Nottingham (Third series)

The reverse of the card reads......................
The Earl of Plymouth
The newly advanced Earl of Plymouth, whose former title of Windsor is still more familiar, is really a scion of the ancient family of Clive. The Barony of Windsor, created in 1529 passed to the Hickmans, the seventh Lord Windsor being created Earl of Plymouth in 1682. This Earldom became extinct in 1843, but the Barony had previously fallen into abeyance, this being terminated in 1855 in favour of Lady Harriet Windsor - Clive, grandmother of the present peer.

She recalls the Shah of Persia's visit in July 1889 also that his table manners were not up to Victorian Standards. Anything he was not happy about he would throw down the table.

The late Ethel Bennet was in service at the Grange after leaving school. Arising at 6.00 a.m. she would attend to all the fire places and collect the wood and coal. After this her duties would be in the kitchens, preparing vegetables and many other tasks, the kitchen sinks were huge, made out of copper and were kept spotless.

She was paid 2/6 (old money) each week plus her keep.

The Earl and Countess of Plymouth attended Tardebigge Church every Sunday when they were in residence. Ethel recalls being stopped by the Earl who asked her if she was better, feeling that she could not accept his offer of a lift to church he then invited her to sit with his family in church.

Tardebigge Church School & Top Lock House - Photo by Peter Hill

After the service she was taken home in a chauffeur driven car, her father was dumbstruck when he saw Ethel stepping out of a car which he had recognised as the Plymouth's family car. Her parents thought she had been taken ill and her mother sternly said "I hope you didn't ask them to bring you home". In the course of conversation which followed Ethel remarked "These things stay in your memory for ever".

Lord Plymouth and Heligoland........................
It is noteworthy to read that Lord Plymouth's genealogical chart begins with a certain OTHERE, a young Viking Chief who owned Heligoland, and it said to have been the discoverer of the North Cape.
It was said that this sea king, OTHERE of HELIGOLAND whom King Alfred describes, and after the King Longfellow.
Ext..... From the Earl of Plymouth's book.
Part of twenty three verse poem by Henry Wordsworth Longfellow was mentioned in Lord Plymouth's book but not the title which is "The Discovery of The North Cape".

A Leaf from King Alfred's Orosius.
Othere, the old sea captain who dwelt in Heligoland,
To King Alfred, the lover of Truth,
Brought a snow white walrus tooth
Which he held in his brown right hand.

His figure tall and stately, like a boy his eye appeared,
His hair was yellow as hay
But threads of silvery grey
Gleamed in his tawny beard.
Hearty and hale was Othere,
His cheeks were the colour of oak.
With a kind of laugh in his speech, like the sea tide on a beach,
As unto the King he spoke.

And Alfred, King of the Saxons
Had a book upon his knees,
And wrote down a wondrous tale
Of him who was first to sail into the Arctic seas.
So far as I live to Northward
No man lives north of me,
To the east are the wild mountain-chains, and beyond them
meres and plains
To the westward all is sea.

So far I live to the northward
From the harbour to Skeringes - hale
If you only sailed by day with a fair wind all the way
More than a month you'd sail.
I own six hundred reindeer
With sheep and swine beside,
Whale bone and reindeer skins
And ropes of walrus hide.

I ploughed the land with horses
But my heart was ill at ease
For the old sea-faring men came to me now and then
With their saga of the seas

And then uprose before me
Upon the water's edge,
The huge and haggard shape of that unknown North Cape
Whose form is like a wedge.

But Othere, the old sea captain

Phyllis - 1923

He neither paused nor stirred
Till the King listened, and then once more took up his pen,
And wrote down every word.

The year 1910 saw the gathering of the Worcestershire Yeomanry in the park at Hewell Grange. They were also known as the Queen's Own Worcestershire Hussars.

Each man was a volunteer, patriotic and devoted to the call of his country mostly land owners and farmers so many were able to bring along their own horses.

Lord Windsor (created Earl of Plymouth 1905) joined the regiment in 1879 and was in command of the Tardebigge troop in 1883 and in 1893 he became Lieut. Colonel and was in command until 1906 the year after he was created Earl of Plymouth.

Such was the enthusiasm of these volunteers that when Lord Windsor issued a Regimental order asking for 126 more men, over 3021 offered their services.

Lord Windsor, spoken of by his employees as a kind and generous man, devoted to his home and family he had a great respect for nature. So great

Maurice Clarke Collection

Ivor   *Windsor*   *Archer*

1910

was his love for conservation that he would go to the utter extreme to protect the birds and other wildlife. My father often related the story of how his Lordship asked for hurdles to be placed around a tree where a bird was sitting, he was afraid the visitors might disturb it.

A group of Total Abstainers (non-drinkers of alcohol) from the Church of England Temperance Society seated on the steps of the Lickey Monument (circa 1890), appear in the photograph opposite.

This was probably a White Ribboners outing travelling in wagonettes or possibly by rail to Barnt Green.

After leaving the railway station people headed for Rednal a start to their days outing on the Lickey Hills, many also travelled from Birmingham to Rednal by tram.

The owner of the hills was Lord Windsor and the Lickey Monument was erected by the Worcestershire Regiment of Yeomanry Cavalry in memory of Other Archer 6th Earl of Plymouth, Colonel Commandant.

The Lickey Hills has always been know as the beauty spot of the Midlands, surrounded by magnificent stately trees in later years covered in bluebells (which one was not allowed to pick).

A city dweller's paradise................

Open countryside, beautiful views and all the fresh air one could wish for. I too have memories of the Lickey Hills in 1941 two student nurses from Selly Oak Hospital set off by tram along the Bristol Road heading for the Lickey Hills, one was nurse Brown the other, yours truly..... As usual I informed Ward Sister on the men's ward "I know where we can get some Holly" Tut Tut, we had also gone out in uniform....!!

We had both picked an enormous bunch of holly as we turned to make our way back to the tram a huge dark figure appeared from out of the blue and a loud voice roared out "And just what do you think you're doing". I was so frightened, I dropped my holly and was speechless, I could hear my heart thumping as he continued to bellow at us...............

Don't you know it's forbidden to pick holly, can't you read the notices?.

Two pairs of brown eyes stood and gazed at this apparition standing before us and then I innocently said "Well, hm, hm well, I did know you are not allowed to pick bluebells and even if we had seen some we wouldn't have picked any".

Oh dear, I thought are we going to spend the night in a cell and get a criminal record.

Gazing at the man's ferocious face I wondered just for a moment, did I

Other in S.Africa - 1907

Worcestershire Yeomanry in camp at Hewell Grange - C.1910
Maurice Clarke Collection

detect a twinkle in those hazel eyes, no it must be my imagination.
"Alright be off with you and just remember my warning".
"Can we take the holly now we've picked it?".
He grunted some remark which I didn't hear and as I gathered up my holly
I said "The ward would look very dull without it".
As we walked away I muttered to my colleague "I'm not going to wish him
a merry Christmas". For a short distance he followed us and suddenly he
said "I don't think any ward would be dull with you two ladies around".
So....... he had got a soft spot..... after....... all.
When we related our adventure to some of the patients we learnt that he
was the park keeper. What me, a student nurse, I didn't even know that such
people existed, I cannot ever recall seeing a park keeper in Hewell Park!!!!

The Redditch Indicator - Saturday, November 11th 1911.
Village Hall at Tardebigge
Generous Gift by Lord Plymouth
A new village hall which has been erected at Tardebigge was opened for use
on Thursday night. The villagers owe the erection of this building to the
generosity of the Earl of Plymouth who conceived the idea of providing a

place where young and old could meet for social intercourse and also for educational purposes. The new hall will meet a much needed want, and the inhabitants are deeply generous to his lordship for once again manifesting a kindly interest in the social life of the people of the district.

The building operations of the new village hall commence in September 1910, and now that it is completed it stands as an ornament to the neighbourhood - a useful ornament, too. Situated on the main road from Bromsgrove to Redditch, near one of the entrances to Hewell Park, and within a stone's throw from Home Farm, the building is within easy distance of residents in various parts of the parish. It is an imposing looking structure, the area of the building and adjacent courtyard being about 1,400 square yards. The actual building stands on little more than half of this area. While as far as possible, modern requirements have been conformed with, the building has been erected in a style adapted to the latter part of the seventeenth century. The whole design depends upon it's simplicity and proportions for its general effect. The building on plan is of the courtyard type with a large main entrance from the road through the building on to the terraces surrounding the courtyard. The accommodation comprises of a concert hall, 63 feet by 30 feet, which is entered from the main archway on the left. This is a spacious and handsome room, with a barrel ceiling which is divided by ribs running across, and supported from the ground by piers which greatly add to the appearance of the room and at the same time support the structure of the roof. A stage has been fitted across the full width of the room. The dimensions of the stage are 15 feet by 30 feet, and it has been made in sections to facilitate removal at any time should the space be required for dancing. In connection with the concert hall, a retiring room has been provided, which it is also intended to use as a ladies reading room. Near this is an entrance hall which gives access also to the concert hall and retiring room, and a kitchen, 25 feet by 25 feet in which demonstrations and lectures will be given on cookery to school children and others. The kitchen has been fitted with an excellent range, and furnished with tables and a large dresser across one end of the room. Lavatory accommodation is also provided in this wing of the building, while over the retiring room and kitchen is a large store room where furniture can be placed. Coming to the right wing of the building, there is a billiard room, access to which is obtained from the right of the main entrance archway. The area of this room is 37 feet by 30 feet. It is a handsome and spacious room. The floor is of polished oak, while there is a cove ceiling, the edges of the cove being finished with a deep cornice on the lower part, finished the top part of the cove with a large moulding. The walls of this room have

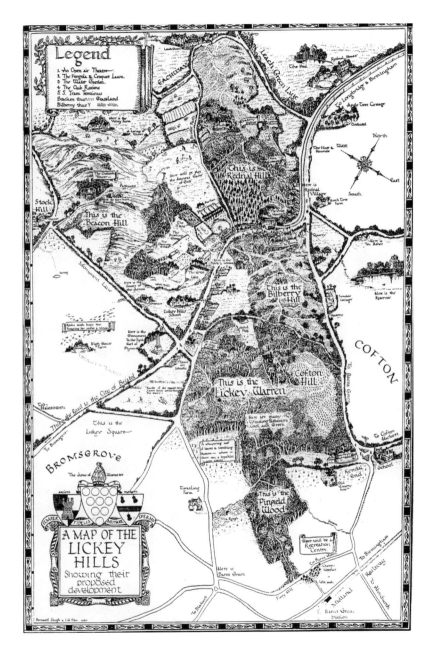

Map of proposed Development 1920

been decorated with heads of a number of wild animals which were shot by the late Viscount Windsor in South Africa. Over the entrance are fixed three stags heads which were obtained from Lord Plymouth's Scottish Estate. Leaving this room and coming along the terrace one enters a hall which leads to the reading room and games room, which is 25 feet by 25 feet. Lavatory accommodation is provided on this wing, including a bathroom with hot and cold water. A handsome oak staircase leads from the hall to a room provided partly in the roof and over the reading room, which will be used for carpentry and wood carving, while near there is a storeroom. The remainder of this wing is utilised for the provision of accommodation for the caretaker. This consists of a hall entrance, parlour, living room, scullery, larder, store and four bedrooms. The whole of the interior of the building is, as regards the plaster work, coloured white, while the woodwork is also painted white. The building is well lighted by large windows. The floor of the concert hall is terrazzo mosaic and the kitchen wood blocks. Double oak doors with handsome bronze furniture and fitted with floor springs are provided in the building. The heating is by low pressure hot water, the pipes being mainly under the building, while the radiators are placed in recesses underneath the window and are arranged in such a way that all the fresh air coming into the building passes through the radiators and is warmed. Electric light has been installed throughout the building, this being supplied from the estate lighting station, while the work of installation was mainly carried out by the estate electricians, the reading room is fitted with bookcases and tables and concert hall birch chairs.

Plaque to other Archer on the Lickey Monument

The building is constructed of thin red brick made on the estate at Mr's Frisby's brickyard. The roof is tiled, surmounted with a large turret over the main entrance, which serves for ventilation as well as ornamentation. The courtyard, which is behind the building from the main road, is surrounded by a terrace on the level of the floor of the building, and the steps lead to the courtyard which is at lower level. The walls of the terrace are of brickwork finished with stone coping. The terrace and steps are paved with stone. An attractive feature of the building on the courtyard side is a verandah which covers the whole of the terrace parallel with the main front, enabling anyone passing from the end of the left wing to the end of the right wing to be under cover. The verandah is formed with the exception of the roof completely of oak beams and posts. Footpaths cross the courtyard, the remainder will be turfed. The whole building is surrounded on the outside by a grass terrace. The building was erected by Messrs. J & A Brazier under the supervision of Mr. Frank Brazier; the heating arrangements were installed by Messrs. J Ward and Sons. Worcester: the leaded lights for the windows were supplied and fixed by Messrs. Swain Bourne and Sons, Birmingham while a portion of the furnishing was done by Messrs. Cranmore, Simmons and Company, Redditch. Mr Francis F. Baylis of Redditch has been the architect, acting under the personal instructions of Lord Plymouth, who has taken a deep, practical interest both in the conception of the design and of the carrying out of the actual construction of the building.

That the new hall will be appreciated is shown by the fact that there are already nearly 350 members. Membership is confirmed to men and women residing in the ecclesiastical parish of Tardebigge, and servants or employees on the Hewell Estate who have attained the age of fourteen. The subscription is 4/- per annum per men and 2/- for women and girls and youths from 14 to 18 years old. The hall is open from 2 to 10 p.m. except Sundays and Good Fridays, when the hours are from two to five and from eight to ten p.m. No intoxicating liquors will be supplied on the premises. Strangers will be admitted to the club if accompanied by a member, upon payment of a penny, but the visitors have to be non - residents of Tardebigge. The committee are empowered to arrange concerts, lectures, classes, meetings, dinners or entertainments. It is not intended to make a charge for parochial gatherings held at the hall. Games and billiards, cards and backgammon etc., will be provided, and books will be added to the library as time goes on Lord Plymouth, who is president, handed over control of the hall to a committee of fifteen, eight who were nominated by himself, five being nominated by the eight committee members and approved by him.

The Monument., The Lickeys, near Barnt Green

Medal Commemorating the death of the 6th Earl of Plymouth
(Other Archer Windsor of Hewell Grange) in 1833.
Designed by Edward Avern.
The 6th Earl was founder and Colonel - in - chief of the Worcestershire
Regiment of Yeomanry Cavalry in 1832. He died of apoplexy
aboard his yatch at Deptford aged 44

Next year it is intended that the committee shall be elected by the members. Mr A.A. Pettigrew is secretary, Mr. H. Bate treasurer, and the committee is composed as follows:- The Earl and Countess of Plymouth, the Rev. Canon Dickins, Miss Dickins, Mr and Mrs. Hugh Dixon, Mr and Mrs L. F. Lambert, Messrs F Buckley, F. Rowles, J Beattie, J Johnson, H Bate, A. A. Pettigrew and A Johnson.

The Opening Ceremony
There was a large attendance at the opening ceremony on Thursday night, the proceedings commenced with tea, which was followed by a meeting and concert in the concert hall. Among those present were The Earl and Countess of Plymouth, Lady Padgett, Lord Windsor, Lady Phyliss Windsor - Clive, Mr and Mrs L F Lambert, Mr M R Margesson, Colonel M Dixon, Mr and Mrs Ralph Dixon, Mr and Mrs Hugh Dixon, Mr and Mrs Harvey Dixon, the Rev Canon and Miss Dickins, Mr Wyekam Musgrave, Mr and Mrs F Bayliss, Messrs F Buckley, T Buckley, H Bate, J G Green, W Hobday, J Brazier, A Brazier, J Harvey, A A Pettigrew, F J Treadgold, A E Shrieves and many others.
In opening the proceedings the Earl of Plymouth who was warmly received, said he was glad to have the opportunity of saying a few words, partly explanatory and partly his good wishes for the future of the enterprise. He thought most of them who lived in the parish had always thought there

were considerable difficulties in gathering together the community because they had no centre. Although the school had been used, and had been found very useful, from the nature of things it was hardly possible to make it an adequate gathering ground and centre for the whole parish. The feeling had been growing stronger and stronger in the mind of Lady Plymouth and himself that a building of that kind would really be of use if their intentions could be carried out. He hoped the building would never be called an institute - (laughter). He did not like the word. He did not quite know what it meant (renewed laughter). He thought that if they went back to the good Anglo - Saxon, and called it a hall, it would be better. They all knew what a town hall meant - it was the centre of the civic life of their ancient boroughs and towns - and why should they not have a hall there as a gathering ground and a meeting place for the community (applause). There were two main objects that they had in view, one was that the hall would be very useful as a centre of the parish, where they could meet and exchange ideas of a more or less serious kind, and where the possibilities of obtaining information and receiving instruction which might be specially useful in the ordinary daily lives of many of them.

That was one side. Then equally important and quite as much to be looked after, was the idea of a place where those who had done a hard days work might meet and spend a few hours in the evening for recreation and enjoyment - (applause). He hoped neither of these two aspects of the use of the hall would be neglected or forgotten. The particular incentive which made Lady Plymouth and himself feel they should undertake this work was that they hoped the parishioners would always connect it closely with the memory of their son (the late Viscount Windsor) who, as they knew great interest in, and sympathy with all those who lived around him. They meant to see that something was placed upon the building which could thus mark it for all time (applause). Continuing Lord Plymouth said he would like to say a word about the admirable manner in which the whole work had been designed and carried out by Mr. Bayliss, the architect. He (Lord Plymouth) was in close touch with him throughout the work. They discussed all details and everything connected with it together, and he would like to say how admirably he had carried out their (Lord and Lady Plymouth's) wishes (applause). Mr Bayliss might feel satisfied that he had erected a building of which the parish might be proud. It was good in design and fulfilled its purpose. It was sound in construction and simple in its ornament and decoration - (applause).

He would also like to add a word of thanks to Mr. Brazier who carried out the work of building, they were glad that so much from the foundation to

The First Hewell Grange - 1716

the roof was purely local. And now, said his Lordship, he only wished to hand it over to be best use of that was possible for the enjoyment and for the benefit of the community of the parish. They wanted to launch the ship on her course and hoped that the hall might benefit many, many generations long after those who were present had played their part in life and passed away.

Whatever changes there might be in the future the parish hall would remain for many generations to be of service to those who were living in that district. He handed it over with the hope that what they thought might be its future would be realised - (applause).

The Rev.Cannon Dickins said it was a real pleasure to him to have been asked to represent the parish on the occasion, and to accept with gratitude that beautiful building, which had attaching to it a sacred memory. There was one drawback to the complete satisfaction which he felt. He would have liked the opportunity of alluding to some things of the past, and expressing gratitude for much excellent work and benefactions of which the family, who Lord Plymouth represented, had been responsible for in the parish - (applause). He referred to the church of St. Philip, Webheath, the church at Lower Bentley, the provision for a stipend for the curate and the schools which were presented to the parish and effectively supported. These were simple instances of various good works of which Lord Plymouth's family had been the authors and for which there was much gratitude. Continuing, Can. Dickins proposed the following resolution:-

Old Ruins Hewell

"We, parishioners of Tardebigge and others working on the Hewell Estate, tender out sincere thanks to the Earl and Countess of Plymouth for their generosity in providing this splendid hall and buildings for the use of the parish". The gift of the hall, said Canon Dickins, in conclusion seemed to put the coping stone on the numerous other works to which he had alluded. These works had for their object the higher side of human life - the spiritual side. Now Lord and Lady Plymouth had supplied the machinery for developing the intellectual and social side of humanity. He had not the slightest doubt that the hall would be freely used and with great advantage - (applause).

In seconding, Mr F Rowles said words failed him in expressing their appreciation of the gift of the beautiful hall. There was, however a better way of returning thanks to Lord and Lady Plymouth. This was by the way they used the hall and the good they would get out of it. Lord and Lady Plymouth had done their part nobly and it remained for them to carry on the work and show that they were not ungrateful of their kindness. They hoped the large attendance at the meeting was a happy omen for the future. They already had a membership of over 330, and hoped to spend many happy evenings together. The duties and privileges of membership did not end with the payment of subscriptions. There was something higher than membership of a place like that. They ought to see that in proportion to the benefits that they received each member took a responsibility for the welfare of the hall and it's work. They ought to be workers and watchers - workers in the sense of doing good to each other, and watchers in the sense of watching over it as something to be extremely proud of, and seeing that it was always well used and never abused - (applause). He hoped Lord and Lady Plymouth would visit them occasionally, and that they would see that they were doing good, social work, and meeting a much needed want in the village. He was sure they would all join him in wishing much prosperity and success to the Tardebigge Village Hall - (applause).

Colonel M. Dixon, in supporting the vote of thanks, said Lord Plymouth's kindness in providing that splendid parish hall was very highly appreciated by all the residents in the parish. In erecting that building he had supplied a want that they had felt for a long time past. It had been uppermost in the minds of a great many of them for some years as to what means they could raise for the provision of a parish hall. They had been quite alive to

The Vacant Chair
A white stone tomb, the inscriptions are engraved on panels of pophyry. Situated in the old churchyard at Tardebigge.
The inscription reads:-
Robert George Earl of Plymouth P.C.
CBE CB
Officer of the Legion of Honour Sub - Prior of the Order of St. John of Jerusalem in England
Born August 27th 1857
- Died March 6th 1923.
Other Robert Vicount Windsor
- Died AGRA Dec 23rd 1908.
Hon Archer Windsor Clive- Lieut Coldstream Guards
Born Nov 6th 1890
Killed in action Aug 25th 1914 at LA.
and lies buried on the battlefield.

the fact that the accommodation that had been available for gatherings had hardly been adequate for the requirements of a large and scattered parish like Tardebigge. That problem had been solved for them by the kindness and generosity of Lord Plymouth in providing that splendid hall - (applause). Everyone who had been over the building could not help being struck with the amount of care and forethought on the part of Lord Plymouth for the requirements both for pleasure and instruction for all grades of society in the parish. With a hall of that description all the differerent grades of society could meet under one roof on a common level - (applause). He could not help thinking that meetings of that sort must be of benefit to the community generally. They met people and they got to know them and respect them. To Lord Plymouth they owed a deep debt of gratitude - (applause). By his action he had added once more to an already long list of noble services which he and his family had rendered to the parish of Tardebigge.

He sincerely hoped that Lord and Lady Plymouth would be spared for many years to live among them, and that as the years rolled by they might witness from time to time the joy and pleasure of those who lived around them, brought about by this act of splendid magnificence which he had performed that evening - (applause). It was a great joy to Lord and Lady Plymouth and he (Colonel Dixon), hoped that, that joy in a way help them to bear the sorrow from which that joy sprang - (applause).

The vote of thanks was accorded, three hearty cheers being given for Lord and Lady Plymouth.

In reply, Lord Plymouth said he thanked them very much for the way in which they had thanked Lady Plymouth and himself. The most gratifying fact that he had to announce that there was already a membership of 153 women and girls, 151 men and 23 youths, while there was 22 candidates making a total membership of 349. This shows how quickly they had come forward to take advantage of what they had been able to provide the parish. They had been obliged to fix a limit of age for membership. Doubtless if that limit had not been as high as fourteen years there would have been many more candidates for admission.

A concert then took place. The programme was an excellent one and was well rendered and highly appreciated. The items were as follows,

Glee - On the Banks of Allan Water - The Colmore Quartet; song - I knew, Miss Emily Cleobury; glee - Genevieve - The Colmore Quartet; violin solo (a) Andantino, (b) Moto Perpetuo - Miss Edser; glee - Spin Spin Swedish Folk song; The Colmore Quartet ; song - The Valley of Laughter Miss Emily Cleobury; glee - O'a the Airts - The Colmore Quartet; song - Three Jolly

Blacksmiths - Mr Sidney Stoddart; violin solo (a) Berceuse (b) Mazur- Miss Edser, duet - Tenor and Baritone - Messrs. Blackburn and Stoddart; glee - Comrades in Arms - The Colmore Quartet.

Tardebigge Village Hall was designed by the Earl of Plymouth, built in memory of his eldest son Other who died at Arga, December 23rd 1908. A. D. C. to the Viceroy, Lord Minton.

The hall was a gift from the Earl of Plymouth.

He always had a deep affection for his home and the welfare of those connected with it was very dear to his heart.

Ext.....Robert George. Earl of Plymouth. 1857 - 1923.

It was also his wish that every girl in the parish should be taught cookery and laundry and every boy should learn woodwork. A place where young and old could meet.

The Earl's final words at the opening speech were "Whatever changes there might be in the future the Parish Hall would remain for many generations to be of service to those who were living in the district".

CHAPTER THREE

Clive of India

It was not until the winter of 1981 that I was able to obtain photographs of the "Bas Reliefs".

At this time the Village Hall was closed and had been so for quite a long time but Ansells Brewery still held the keys.

It was arranged for me to meet up with the Area Manger to gain access.

It was obvious that the hall had been closed for a considerable length of time. There was a dank musty smell about the place, curtains still hung at the windows, fading and rotting, the building was cold and dreary and made me feel as I was standing there very depressed and very miserable and I had no wish to linger or to reminisce, lets take the photo's and get out of the place, but the light and the equipment was poor, still in this day and age wonders can be worked so I must hope for the best.

I must now concentrate on the research relating to my hero "Clive of India". Robert Clive 1st Baron 1725 - 1774.

English soldier and administrator, born at Styche near Market Drayton on 19th September. Educated at the Merchant Taylor school and the despair of his teachers.

Sent to Madras at the age of 18 as a writer in the East India Company's service.

When La Bourdonnais took Madras in 1746 Clive escaped to Fort St David twenty miles to the south.

Under the watchful eye of Major Stringer, Lawrence father of the Indian Army, he learned the military profession and was appointed ensign in the 2nd Company of foot soldiers.

At this time the French and English were intriguing with the country powers and supporting rival candidates for the post of "Nawab of the Carnatic". When Chanda Sahib, the French nominee was blockading the fort at Trichinopoly, held by a weak British battalion and the defenders were at their last gasp Clive had the brilliant idea of attacking Arcot, Chanda Sahib's capital, this was successful and Chanda Sahib was forced to return but Clive himself was besieged in Arcot which he held for fifty three days.

Chanda Sahib was defeated and put to death and Mohammed Ali, the English nominee was installed as Nawab.

In 1753 Clive married Margaret Maskeleyne and returned to England. Two years later he was sent out as Governor to Fort St. David. On the way he

Clive receives the Grant of Bengal Behar and Orissa
at Allahabad - August 1763

stopped at Bombay with Admiral Watson and took part in the reduction of the Maratha pirate stronghold of Gheria.

When he arrived at Madras he was confronted with the news of the capture of Clacutta and the tragedy of the "Black Hole" where many European men, women and children died of suffocation.

Clive was now determined to dispose of Siraj-ud-daula who was responsible for the tragedy of Calcutta and replace him with his own nominee Mir-Ja'far but a Sikh banker of the name Omichund (Amin Chand) threatened to betray the scheme but was duped by means of a forged copy of the treaty, promising him twenty lakhs or rupees.

Clive marched out to meet his opponent and on the 23rd June 1757, at Plassey with 3200 men and nine guns he routed Siraj-ud-daula and his force of 50,000 men and fifty three guns, for the loss of less than eighty killed and wounded.

Clive entered Murshidabad, the capital of Mogul viceroys and installed Mir Ja'far as Nawab. The palace treasury was loaded with riches and Clive was afterwards accused of accepting large sums of money. He returned to England in 1750, he was thirty five and had a fortune of £300,000 also the "quit rent" of the lands around Calcutta amounting to £27,000 per annum. He was received by Pitt and the king who in 1762 made him Baron - Clive of Plassey.

These panels were placed here by the members of the Tardebigge Village Hall in memory of and in gratitude to Robert George Earl of Plymouth - Born August 27th 1857, Died March 6th 1923

In 1761 he entered Parliament as member for Shrewsbury. During his absence the government of Bengal broke down and at Patna the whole of the company's servants were massacred at the order of the Nawab's son in law by the Swiss mercenary named Samru.

Clive went out as Governor of Bengal and commander in chief, and at Benares on August 12th he received from the hand of the Emperor Sha Alam a "firman" granting the company the "diwani" or right of revenue collection for Bengal, Bihar and Orissa.

By this means the East India Company became the "de facte" ruler over thirty million people with an annual revenue of four million pounds sterling.

He reformed the administration, the miserable salaries of the company's servants were raised and a check put on private trade and the receipt of presents, the army was reformed and "batta" field service allowance were reduced.

Clive's drastic measures had made him a host of enemies in England, where the growing political influence of the "Nawabs" was much apprehended.

On his return to England his proceedings were made the subject of an inquiry by a select committee of the House of Commons. Clive was deeply indignant and complained that he had been treated more like a sheep stealer that the founder of an empire. The select committee while not exonerating him, found that Robert Lord Clive did, at the same time, great and meritorious service to his country.

He died probably by his own hand in 1774.

His eldest son, Edward Clive, 1st Earl of Powis, 1754 - 1839, was governor of Madras from 1798 to 1803.

Ext G.B. Malleson's "Life of Lord Clive".

Sir G.W. Forrest's "Life of Lord Clive".

Cambridge History of India - Volume 5.

The story of Lord Clive was often related in the history of the Plymouth family during my school days.

In 1784 Lord Clive's son married Henrietta Antonia Herbert, Countess of Powys.

Many of the collections made by Lord Clive during his military triumphs in India can now be seen in the National Trust monument Powys Castle.

Local folk lore has informed me, on more that one occasion, that Clive of India's horse was stuffed and mounted and in later years was kept in the stables at Hewell Grange. One of the kitchen maids, working at the grange was terrified of horses, so, whenever she could see her chance and also knew that she would not be missed, she would wait until the stables were empty and without anyone knowing proceed to groom the animal.

One thing she was quite sure of.......She wouldn't get kicked.......

Fact or fallacy..........Who knows?...........................

During the Great War years the Bas Relief sculptures were removed to Hewell Grange for safe keeping.

They were not put on show on the walls of the village hall until early in 1920.

CHAPTER FOUR

Tardebigge V. A.D. Hospital 1914

An ODE written in 1746

How sleep the brave sink to rest
By all their country's wishes blest,
When spring, with dewey fingers cold,
Returns to deck their hallow'd mould,
She there shall dress a sweeter sod
Than fancy'y feet have ever trod.

By fairy hands their knell is rung,
By forms unseen their dirge is sung
Their Honour comes a pilgrim grey,
To bless the turf that wraps their clay,
And freedom shall awhile repair
To dwell, a weeping hermit, there.

W. Collins 1721 - 1759.

1914

My father had moved to Tardebigge from Worcester to take a lock keepers job in 1912.

In 1916 he became a Water Baliff for the Bournville Angling Club at a salary of £3.00 per annum.

Tardebigge Reservoir formed part of the Hewell Estate, the punt and oars were made from timber which was cut from the trees. The Earl of Plymouth was a conservationist, he disliked the thought of any disturbance of the Flora and Fauna.

Although happy to serve his country he was far more contented to watch the kingfishers swooping and diving into the lake or listen to the singing of the nightingale, always careful to instruct the workmen not to disturb the nesting birds.

As the church bells rang in the New Year many people were wondering just what 1914 would mean to them. So early in that year my father set out to

1914-1918 Tardebigge V.A.D. Hospital & Patients

deliver some papers to leave at Hewell Grange to be signed. As he was walking down through Hewell Park he met the Earl who said, "The news is not good Warner, I'm afraid the Balkans have become a problem, it is a sorry state of affairs, there is much bitterness and confusion, new wars are breaking out between small countries, it only needs one small spark to extinguish the lamps all over Europe. I pray to God this will never happen, but if it does it will be a very long war".

My father never forgot the Earl of Plymouth's words. Many years later he often said "The Earl was right, you know, it is a very long war"!!!

On a Sunday morning in June 1914 Archduke Franz Ferdinand, heir to the Austrian throne was assassinated whilst on a visit to Sarajevo, the small town in Bosnia, that later became know as Yugoslavia, like a damp squib wating to ignite, Austria took revenge on Serbia and before another month had passed England was at war.

Even although this tragic event shook the world the severity of it was little thought of in England and a season of annual events in London was in full swing, The Trooping of the Colour, the Queen's Birthday Parade held on the 4th July had just taken place.

Wimbledon was in full swing and the Derby at Epsom in Surrey had been won by "Durbar".

Along the banks of the river Thames the Henley Royal Regatta had once again attracted a large crown of wellwishers. Tall young men dressed in white flannels, white shirts and straw boaters walked hand in hand with elegant young ladies in long flowing dresses made out of delicate lawn (fine cotton) the colours of their dresses with the sun shining down on them stood out like hues of the rainbow, their straw hats trimmed with assorted coloured ribbons hanging down their back completed a perfect picture.

How many of these young men were to guess that they would soon be serving their country and would carry in their memory the picture of today's events with them.

For many of them this would be their FINAL Regatta....................

They went with songs to battle. They were young,
Straight of limb, true of eye, steady and aglow,
They were staunch to the end against odds uncounted,
They fell with their faces to the foe.

They mingle not with their laughing comrades again.
They sit no more at familiar tables at home,
They have no lot in our labour of the day-time.
They sleep beyond England's foam.

Taken from Laurence Binyon's poem "For the Fallen".

Suddenly preparations for war began, any suitable building became a recruitment office, all factories were working round the clock to produce ammunitions, tanks and all available iron and steel was collected to be melted down, not a scrap of metal was wasted and large loads were transported by barges along the canals.

My father was responsible for the movement of this transport and to make sure that no precious time was lost.

He was not eligible for "call-up" having had both his "trigger fingers" smashed in an accident when he started work at the age of twelve years in 1881.

He became a Special Constable and his main duties were towards the smooth running of canal transport.

In 1929 he was awarded a long service medal.

Not wishing to disclose their real names they often gave the name of Tommy Atkins, a name which became attached throughout the years for a private in the British Army.

Pity any poor lad who happened to have ginger hair he would be taunted by his mates singing to him........

Ginger, you'r balmy

Back view of Hospital

Why don't you join the army?
Even the music halls were quick to make jokes, one such tale was.......
The child who said.....
"What did you do in the Great War daddy?"
The father replied
"I held you while your mother sold flags".......
Recruiting posters were placed on every available wall and building and every fit man between the ages of 18 and 45 was expected to serve his country.
Each man took an oath and promised to serve his King and Country and accepted one shilling (5p) as a token of agreement, but in 1916 the government was forced to introduce compulsory military service.
To some men the idea of killing was appalling, these were classed as conscientious objectors and were forced to appear before a tribunal yet many "conchies" were willing to serve as front line as ambulance drivers and stretcher bearers risking their lives to help the troops.
It was Lord Kitchener who persuaded the men to "Take the Kings Shilling" and in 1915 Wills produced a series of cigarette cards commonly knows as the "Faggies" telling the men to.............
Follow me.......Rally round the flag......Do your bit......Answer now your country's hour of need......

Our own Worcestershire Regiment, like so many other regiments, had so many tragic tales to tell.

Tales of the scarred Somme battlefields, Ypres where poison gas was first used, Loos, Gallipoli and the dreaded No Mans Land but their main nostalgic story was the battle in October 1914 to recapture the Chateau Gheluvelt in Belgium. This was an incredible achievement considered an impossible task, it is still talked about today with pride, cherished memories of Victoria Crosses, that were won and comrades sadly remembered with a tear.

As a small child the long summer holidays from school, were spent with my Aunt and Uncle (the Watton family) at Diglis locks Worcester.

Often on a warm summer evening we would walk from Diglis along the banks to the River Severn toward Gheluvelt park, the name of the park which was framed in a wrought iron horse shoe shape over the main gate had so oftened fascinated me.

It was, many years later when I discovered it's origin.

In the trenches men dreamed of returning to "Blighty" their homes in Britain, they prayed that their houses would not be destroyed by a German Zeppelin (an airship designed by Germany to carry bombs) named after F. Von. Zeppelin a German inventor, designed about 1900.

They had no idea what a different "Blighty" they would return to when they were given a spell of leave.

A new act had been passed "The Defence of the Realm" commonly known as DORA. This act enabled the Government to make drastic changes using it's power over the mines and railways.

There was to be no waste, seamen were risking their lives to bring food, the throwing of bread to pigeons was prohibited, drinking hours in Public Houses were strict and it was forbidded to treat one's friends.

Women joined the Land Army, they joined the fire fighters, they drove the coal waggons, worked as tram conductors, kept the ammunition factories going twenty four hours a day, in fact anything that their men could do they could do and were willing to help the war effort.

Every one was encouraged to grow their own food, millions of people stood for hours queing for food and were often disappointed.

It was during this period of time that our own King George V who was related to German royal family changed his name from Hanover to Windsor.

Many young lads who went to enlist gave fictious dates of birth, some even managed to get away with it, fed up with being unemployed the idea of serving their country and the thought of being able to travel abroad filled their heads with many dreams which were sometimes quickly shattered.

These stories told to me over the last fifty years by ex-servicemen were

hastily scribbled down on any little bit of paper which I was lucky to have
in my pocket at that present moment in time, a shop receipt, the back of a
dental appointment card, a reminder of when I should attend the next
lecture or meeting.

All so old now they have either gone yellow with age or sprouted
whiskers!!!.......

Many of them required a magnifying glass yet it only requires one word to
jog the memory.

Such was the story of the Battle of Gheluvelt Chateau in Belgium, standing
in direct line with the Menin Road.

It was a gory story which took place during the first year of the war. The
Germans had broken through the weak British line and had taken the
village of Gheluvelt, the plan was to descend on the British ports to cut off
the British supplies. Orders were given for the battalion of men from the
Worcestershire Regiment to recapture Gheluvelt ... at all costs ... so it was
"Right lads, in at the double, fixed bayonets", racing through a barrage of
whatever the enemy liked to throw at them, a stormy, bloody battle took
place around Gheluvelt Chateau and the village was recaptured.

Once again many blinds were drawn on too many windows and many tears
were shed back in Blighty.

This story has always been one of the finest related by the Worcestershire
Regiment, and many ghostly shadows linger over Gheluvelt Park in
Worcester.....

CHAPTER FIVE

1914 Onward

During the First World War Tardebigge Village Hall was used as a hospital for wounded soldiers and sailors and known throughout the village as the V.A. D. Hospital (Voluntary Aid Detachment).

It was the local lads of the village who set about scrubbing the highly polished floors until the wood was almost restored to it's natural state of unseasoned wood.

Suddenly the hall was transformed from a place of pleasure to a place of pain, orders were received from the War Department, hospital equipment appeared as if by magic, blankets and bed linen seemed to rain down from the skies. All the windows were blacked out, curtains and outside lighting were removed, suddenly a ghostly hush descended over the building.

Staff began to appear, many were local people and many offered their services voluntary. The nursing staff were the V.A.D.'s, meaning Voluntary Aid Detachment, formed in 1909, these young ladies were strictly supervised under the watchful eye of their Commandant, many of them were daughters of ministers, gentlemen farmers, land owners and often titled people.

Many had attended finishing schools in Germany and Switzerland, their days consisted of tennis parties, theatre outings, dances, afternoon tea in the drawing room, they never washed a cup or made their own beds and yet they craved for excitement, many had joined the Red Cross, The St. John Ambulance Brigade or The Ladies Nursing Yeomanry to gain some knowledge which would later serve as useful medical training, other wanted to leave behind the strict rules of the Victorian Era which dominated their homes, in this way they would learn a little more about the world outside,many would shrink away in horror at the sight of a cut finger, others were taught right from the start, some had helped to nurse relatives in their homes but, whatever the outcome they were determined to master it, like all nursing it was a challenge and to walk into whatever lay ahead with very little knowledge was something to be proud of and so the day dawned when they set out for the experience of a life time, raw recruits, putting on a brave face !!!

Many travelled by train to reach their final destinations. It was on the railway stations that they came face to face with reality and this was only the start, they were faced with poignant scenes as they were pushed and jostled amongst the largest crowds that they had ever seen.

There were armed personnel from all the services mingling with mothers, wives, sweethearts, children, grannies and relatives, many of them crying, all anxious to hug their loved ones and to say their last goodbyes. Many of the troops had no idea of their destinations or whether they would ever see their loved ones again. Many of the nurses had no idea where they too were bound but they were anxious to "do their bit" and having read so many posters they were now ready to "Answer Now Your who Country's Hour of Need". Those that finally found themselves at Tardebigge Village Hall were soon busy putting into practice all their skills, this is what they had waited for.

Early in 1915 the first patients arrived by Red Cross ambulances, kitted out in their hospital blue suits and finally when tucked in between clean white sheets, they thought they were in Paradise......

Many had lost limbs others had severe abdominal wounds, others were suffering from severe exhaustion, they carried their few belongings in a small linen bag that the nurses at the field hospitals had quickly made, most of them had lost everything that they had set out with including their metal mirrors.

Many of the lads clung to what little souvenirs they had not wanting to let them out of their sight, a ribbon for the baby they had left behind and the most treasured of all that small token a dying mate had pressed into the palm of their hand as they expressed a dying wish that it be passed onto their loved one at home with a message.

Many had a tag tied to their tunics a label with a broad red stripe meant "HAEMORRHAGE" this told the stretcher bearer and medical staff to handle with care.

The battle of the Somme in 1916 was the bloodiest so far, many of the wounded too horrific to mention, no one realised that the following year the 3rd battle of Ypres (known to men as Wipres) would be far worse, this was the Battle of Passchendale. When the British troopes captured Messines Ridge one million tons of explosive were used, the roar was heard in London as well, over one hundred miles away.

Many of the troops close at hand lost their hearing, others were literally blown to pieces others received injuries which they would take to their graves, even although this happened 81 years ago there are men still living to tell these stores which many of them have related to me.

April 1915, the date which recorded the use of poison gas.

One afternoon father set out from home to take fresh fruit, vegetables, and eggs for the lads at the village hall.

His large wicker basket which he used only for market days or auction sales was overflowing, he was in his glory at an auction sale and my mother owned more chamber pots and flower vases than any one else in the district.

Father was indeed a familiar figure walking home in the evening with a basket full of chamber pots balanced on his head, they were also referred to as "guzunders". I recall on one occasion saying "Golly, those are pretty, some have roses and some have pansies".

Don't matter my lassie what's painted on them, they will all go the same way home, when the winter comes and the frost freezes the contents in them when they "guzunder" the bed they will all come out chipped, cracked or broken.

After he had unloaded his produce in the hall kitchen he went outside to pass the time of day with some of the lads who were enjoying the afternoon sunshine, careful not to talk about the horrors of the battlefield he chatted for a few minutes about the weather and how smart they all looked in their "Hospital Blue Suits".

He then quietly asked, "Did any of you lads meet or see an Army Padre known as "Woodbine Willie"? Yes, many of the lads had met him and were eager to talk about him.

"The Rev. Geoffrey Studdart Kennedy was vicar of St. Pauls - Worcester when we lived in Lowesmoor at a house on the canal called "The Blockhouse" so we were in his parish".

Most of the lads had been in Woodbine Willies's company at one time or another and he was very well thought of.

The Reverend Geoffrey Studdart Kennedy was born in Leeds, June 27th 1883 where his father was a vicar in a poverty stricken area.

It was his ambition to follow in his father's footsteps but his unorthodox methods were frowned upon by many, as a small boy he was surrounded by poverty, as one of the lads told my father he would take the shirt off his own back to give it to someone less fortunate.

The British Tommies idolised him, his pulpit was an old ammunition box, his message, clear, simple and understood by all. He joined the men in the evening whenever possible, a pub, a derelict farmhouse, a railway station, anywhere where "Two or three are gathered together in His name".

As the trains pulled out of the railway station he would be left with handfulls of names and addresses of loved one back home to contact and tell them that he had seen their dear ones before they departed for the front.

Although he was a man with a warm sunny smile he often left these gatherings with a heavy heart and asked himself how many of these men would return, many of them would be deprived of their independence, speech and motion, how many would turn to God to quote the words of one of our best loved hymns........

Be thou my guardian and my guide
And hear me when I call.
Let not my slippery footsteps slide
And hold me when I fall.

He had heard about the mud and the trenches and the men "going over the top", he asked himself and searched his soul for an answer, "How many of these would his God save"?

How many would he meet again, little did he know then that he would volunteer to become their Army Chaplain and as Christmas drew near in 1915 he found himself travelling to Rouen in France.

Once again he would be concerned with the welfare of troops, handing out those immortal packets of "Woodbines" which earned him the name of "Woodbine Willie". This name had been handed down for the last 80 years. His sole concern was for the welfare of the men and to keep their morale up, in the evenings he would entertain them with such songs as "Roses of Picardy", "Now the Day is Over".

The Tommies' favourite song was,

Dearest the day has ended
Endless the dream divine.
You must go back to your life
I must go back to mine
Tell me again you love me
Kiss me on the lips and brow
Star of my soul I need thee
How can I leave you now.

How can I live without you
How can I let you go.
I that you love so well
You that I worship so
You that I worship so.

Time was often short, not knowing what could happen next so he often used to mix the verses of the songs, which made them very emotional but he was not afraid to show his emotions and the men admired him for this.

At 7.30am. on July 1st 1916 Kitcheners's army went over the top, he was involved in tending his wounded comrades at the attack on Messines Ridge for which he was awarded the Military Cross but it was The Battle of the Somme which really shattered his faith, the sight of thousands of men crossing the hell hole of No Mans Lane, the mud, the blood and the mangled bodies, this he could never forget.

A war to end wars so it was called but to himself he questioned it and wondered!!!

Woodbine Willie was a padre - poet.

He accepted a post in London and died suddenly at the early age of 45 in 1929.

The coffin was transported partly by ferry to Worcester, just as it was about to leave an elderly man walked forward and placed a small item on the top..... It was a packet of Woodbines.....

I think my father must have told this story about Woodbine Willie's last journey each time

SWEET ADELINE (1).

In the evening when I sit alone a-dreaming
Of days gone by, love, to me so dear,
There's a picture that in fancy oft appearing,
Brings back the time, love, when you were near;
It is then I wonder where you are, my darling,
And if your heart to me is still the same,
For the sighing wind and nightingale a-singing,
Are breathing only your own sweet name.

Sweet Adeline (1)

In the evening when I sit alone a-dreaming, of the days gone by, love, to me so dear,

There's a picture that in fancy oft appearing,

Brings back the time love, when you were near,

It is then I wonder where you are darling,

And if your heart to me is still the same,

For the sighing wind and nightingale a-singing

Are breathing only your sweet name.

(Bamford & Co. - England & New York)

he was offered a Woodbine.
Out of all his poems the following impressed me very much.

<u>I lost my Lord</u>

I lost my Lord and sought him long
I journeyed far and cried
His name to every wandering wind,
But still my Lord did hide.

I sought him where the doctors meet
To turn deep questions o'er
But every answer tempted me
To ask one question more.

I sought him where the hermit kennels
And tells his beads of pain
I found him with some children
In my own green leafy lane ………

Early one morning a young lad was found in a most distressing condition.
The night nurse tried many ways to calm him and thought to
herself.............
"Poor wee laddie, he's only a baby yet he's seen it all".
"The mules, the mules", he muttered over and over again.
"I shall remember their eyes until I die. I was a farm hand until I went to
war, it's the animals I feel sorry for, to watch them sink in a sea of liquid mud
their eyes pleading with us and we couldn't do a thing to help them, some
of the men went down with them".
"Poor boy", said the nurse after the lad had got it off his chest, "No wonder
his hair is standing on end".

I too recall, as a young girl, a man who came to visit my father, I had seen
pictures in comic magazines of young boys who had seen something
"scary" and it had made their hair stand on end.
After the man had left I remarked to my father,
"That man look as if he had had a fright", to which my father replied "He's
had more than a fright, he was Chauffeur to the great "Lawrence of Arabia".

Author's note...........................

THOMAS EDWARD LAWRENCE 1888 - 1935

A British soldier with a considerable knowledge of the Middle East Archaeologist 1912, Middle East, who later became an army intelligence officer in Egypt. Later appointed Colonel.

He led the Arab uprising against the Turks during the First World War and became the legendary figure known as "Lawrence of Arabia" (of the desert campaign).

He met with a motor cycle accident which even until today remains a mystery.

"Now then lads", remarked a patient early one morning, "Christmas is coming and the Goose is getting fat, better start thinking about a bit of entertainment, I'm sure you've all got hidden talents lurking away somewhere"!!!

"Well there's a good selection here, to start with Stan's got his melodeon, Dave's got a Jews harp, Bill's got a Gramophone, Hamish has got his bagpipes and then one or two of the lads have got things we don't know about".

One sleepy voice spoke up from underneath the bedclothes "I've got a mouth organ" it was young Taffy.

"Blimey" said one "He's alive, well he must be he's just spoke, don't have much to say do you Taffy?".

"Leave the chap alone, he's a bit homesick, he'll come round in his own sweet way".

The chatter continued on throughout the morning, by then they were getting interested and a programme was roughly made out of different items that could be offered to cheer thing up a bit.

"Why not ask that young nurse to sing, you know the very thin one, the one that Bill calls "Skinny Liz".

"Cor I've heard her singing when the Dragon's not around, cor she sings like a nightingale does that one, she's lovely".

One of the young lads was listening to what was going on, spoke up and said "Me muvver sez you shouldn't call anyone, She, its rude, She's the cats muvver and it's rude".

This was greeted with a chorus of banter and much laughter and remarks like, "Allright teacher we won't do it again" and "Oh, hark at the professor talking".

Those who were able to walk round the lanes would collect pieces of holly and ivy to give the ward a homely festive appearance. As preparation went ahead for the Christmas Concert there were certain items that had to be considered.

It was suggested that they try and keep away from the old familiar war songs, in the words of one of their patients they had, each one......Packed up their troubles in their old kit bags, and they all knew it was a long way to Tipperary, all they asked for was.............A ship that bound for Blighty...........Where the black eyed Susans grow.

"Well" said Dave "I'm very fond of that song that Woodbine Willie sang to us, I forget what it was called now, just let me think for a minute, ah, I remember Mother Macree, that was it".

Even although the lads tried to brush aside the horrors of the battlefields they could not hide the pain in the faces all around them. They spoke of the herioc deeds and if a certain "Tommy Atkins" would ever get a medal for "loyalty to the flag".

It was every man's dream to be awarded the Victoria Cross. The design was chosen by Queen Victoria in 1856, the most coveted medal in the world, cast in broze with two simple words....."For Valor".

Even today it it still cast in bronze from the cannons which were fired at the battle of Sevastopol.

The distinctive purple ribbon worn on the left breast of any man whatever rank or grade stands out above all other. The V.C. has never been won by a woman.

Yet every man and woman had some heroic tale to tell, every woman dreams about her hero, every man dreams about his heroine, many were the stories they could tell about heroic deeds, some of the patients had met up with the "heroine of their dreams, one of the patients, a Yorkshire lad told the story of Flora Sandes, a vicars daughter who spent her entire childhood wishing that she had been born a boy.

After returning from finishing school she longed for excitement and before 1914 became interested in medical training.

At the start of the war she became very downhearted as her training was not accepted for any hospital service, she was determined not to let this disappointment stand in her way and when she heard that the wife of one of Serbia's misinsters was looking for nursing volunteers to help with Serbia's worn torn army she knew this was the answer to her prayers, within a few days she found herself on the train heading for the Balkans.

So Private Flora Sandes was promoted to Corporal and was allowed to use a lightweight carbine rifle, the only English nurse with the Serbian army treating the wounded in the Field ambulance unit where she had fallen victim to a typhus epidemic and recovered.

She kept her diary up to date and along with the men she endured the cold, hunger, mud and filth and lice infection. No wonder she became his heroine.

In 1916 she was promoted to Sergeant and finding it very hard to accept the horrors of war. Night marches consisted of fixed bayonets and eventually her right leg and arm were torn by shrapnel.

Flora Sandes was awarded the Kara George Star, the highest Serbian award and known to that country as the Serbian V.C.

So many times she defied fate, survived Spanish Flu, conquered atrocious was wounds, the Army was her life,...............

Authors Note

In 1919 she became Second Lieutenant Flora Sandes - even to this day she is still a legend in Yugoslavia.

One of the older patients had listened with great interest to the Yorkshire lad talking about his heroine, as the others sat quietly wondering who would tell the next story the older man said "My heroine was nurse Edith Cavell, now there's a lady for you, lived quite close to my hometown she did, last I heard about her was that she was teaching doctors and nurses, had a hard life, she did and met with a violet end. Ah well, she knew what would happen if she got caught helping allied soldiers escape from Belgium, she know the odds, poor lass, I still say she didn't deserve to be shot, I was very sad about that, still am if it come to that. (executed Oct 12th 1915).

She was buried in Belgium and a wooden cross marked her grave.

Authors note

After the war her remains were brought to England for interment. Westminster Abbey was suggested but in May 1919 her remains were laid to rest in Norwich Cathedral.

"Well now has anyone elso got any heroines they would like to get of their chest before we get down to sortin out this Christmas Concert or else you'll all be discharged before we've sorted things out.

Oh no, Tommy Atkins over there wants to have a word, the rest of you can go back to sleep, at this rate we'll never get anywhere, come on then, as me ma used to say "Spit it out".

"You'll ave to go easy with im", said one of the lads, "he stutters".

"Well at this rate we'll be here all night, go back to sleep laddie and we'll sort it out in the morning".

By this time the lad had dozed off again but another lad spoke up, "I'm alway dreaming about Vera Britain, me dad come from Derbyshire where she lived".

"E was allys on about 'er, she went away to be a "nus", me dad thought she wus a smasher, that's why I dreams about 'er.

Had a very tragic life she did, while working at the London Hospital caring for injured men from the battlefields she lost 'er sweetheart. Then she lost 'er sweetheart's besf friend, after that me dad didn't tell me much about her".

Authors note

After the war she returned to Oxford and after graduating her ambition was to become a writer. She wrote many books, in the year 1925 she married and had two children. Shirley Williams, the politician was her daughter (now Baroness Williams of Crosby).

"Come on now lads, any more ideas about this concert".

"Might be a good idea to ask the padre to do a turn in the Christmas Show".

"Do you think he would?"

"You can always ask, no harm done".

"We'll be having a carol service the night before, every body sing up, put your back into it".

"We'll all be so hoarse we'll have no voices left".

Having all decided as to what they could offer by now they were becoming quite enthusiastic about it, there would be no rehearsals, after all it was just a bit of fun, something else to think about and after all they had endured they were entitled to it.

CHAPTER SIX

Christmas Eve

So the Padre, bless him, began with his opening speech,
"A very pleasant evening at this Christmas tide and may the Lord watch over
you, I had very little time to prepare for this night so I'll give you one verse
of "The Miner's Dream of Home".

While the joyous bells rang I wandered my way to the cottage
My home when a boy.
I looked through the window and there by the fire
Sat my parents, my heart filled with joy.
The tears ran down my rugged worn cheeks,
As I gazed at my mother so dear.
I knew in my heart she was saying a prayer
For the boy whom she knew was not near.

"Come on lads sing up ....

I saw the old homestead and faces I love
I saw England's valleys and dells,
I listened with joy as I did when a boy
To the sound of the old village bells.

The log was burning brightly
Twas a night that would banish all sin,
For the bells were ringing the old year out
And ringing the New Year in.

This was greeted by a stamping of feet and much applause.
"Right lads, who's next?

On to the stage stepped a young lad who said,
"I'm a cockney, I am missing me plate of jellied eels, I've pushed me barrer
through the streets of London"......
"Tell us another one, your no cockney".
"I was born within the St. Mary - le - Bow church, Bow Bells.

Hédé Paris - 1918

Now one of the lads in the audience knew a bit of cockneyslang and he whispered to one of the others, "We'll have a bit of fun with this one".
"Right, cockney lad, what's a candle?"
"Arry Randle".
"What's the stairs?"
"Apple and pairs".
"Don't keep askin me, cigarettes are Coffin Nails, me shirt a Dicky Dirt me mates, Mi O'l China and me Ma's old lodger an Artful Dodger".

By now they were all quite convinced that he was a cockney.
"Come on give the lad a bit of applause, thank you cockney lad"........

The next turn was Hamish with his bagpipes who began by playing that lovely old Scottish air by Robert Burns, My Love is Like a Red Red Rose followed by the Flowers of the Forest.
This was greeted with much applause.
This was followed by a small poem by Robert Burns "I'll go and be a Sodger".

O why the deuce should I reoine

1919

Card Reads - Dear Sweetheart, I send you this card with my best wishes for a Happy Christmas to you and all at home. From Harry - 1918.

And be an il foreboder?
I'm twenty three and five foot nine,
I'll go and be a sodger. (soldier)

I gat some gear with mickle (much) care
I held it weel thegither (well together)
But now it's gone and something mair (more)
I'll go and be a sodger

Robert Burns (1759 - 1796)

Hamish finished his turn with that lovely old Scottish song...........
2nd Verse

Farewell to the mountains high covered with snow,
Farewell to the straths and green valleys below,
Farewell to the forests and wild hanging woods,
Farewell to the torrents and loud pouring floods.

"Come on boys sing up,"
My heart's in the highlands, my heart is not here,
My heart's in the highlands a - chasin that deer,
A -chasin the wild deer and following the roe,
My heart's in the highlands wherever I go ....

After the singing there were a few quiet moments while they all lubricated their throats. Stan who played the melodeon was wheelchair bound, he surprised everyone by suddenly saying "I was just sitting here thinking to myself that my favourite show is on in London at the Daly Theatre "The Maid of the Mountains" wonder if I'll ever get up to London again "ah, we'll see what the future holds.
"Come on lads", replied Bill "let's keep ourselves in good spirit on a Christmas Eve" and so they all sang.........

At seventeen he falls in love quite madly with eyes of tender blue,
At twenty four he gets it rather badly with eyes of a different hue,
At thirty five you'll find him flirting madly with two or three or more

When he fancies the he's past love it is then he meets his last love
And he loves her like he's never loved before.

Well the sound of the singing followed by the applause was enough to raise the roof I'm sure they could be heard in Bromsgrove.
"Right, quiet please lads, you'll frighten Santa Claus away".

Now all this frivolity had aroused the young lad, who up until this present moment had been living in a land of his own, he was suffering from shell - shock (now known as combat fatigue). He suddenly sat upright in bed and sang in a loud voice.......

The bells of hell go ding a ling a ling
Go ding a ling a ling, for Jerry (Germans) and for me.
Go ding a ling a ling, go ding a ling
Go ding a ling a ling, go dong ding ding.

"Oh will somebody keep him quiet, he ding a ling a lings all day and half the night, I shall take him and 'is ding a ling a ling and loose him outside".
"Ah leave the kid alone, aint got much of a future as e, ay, his sister came to see him she told me he told the Recruiting Serg he was seventeen and a harf so the serg sez come back when your eighteen so he goes back the next day and sezs he's eighteen and the serg winks his eye to the lad and gives him the King's shilling".

After all the rumpus had died down and the lad had "Ding a ling a linged" himself back to sleep it was a question of whose next.
While they were trying to decide who would make the next move (the concert was unrehearsed) out of the gloom at the top of the ward appeared a shadow and before anyone could speak the cockney lad shouted "Oh me barnet fair (head of hair) it's Skinney Liz and indeed it was Skinney Liz the tall thin V.A.D. with a long dark curtain hanging from her shoulders, a band of coloured ribbons and some paper flowers in her hair - she became the star of the show, a morale booster - the best tonic which men could be given and she sang "Joshua" that lovely old Victorian ballad. You could have heard a pin drop, not even the sound of "ding a ling a ling" came from the corner of the ward......

Joshua, Joshua why don't you call and meet Papa
He'd be pleased to know you are my best beau.
Joshua, Joshua, nicer than lemon squash you are
Oh by gosh you are, Joshu - osh - u - ah.

After the applause had died down one of the lads was heard to say "Cor, told ya I did, cor, got a voice like a nightingale that one", to which every one agreed.
By now the evening was drawing to a close, the lads had spent a lovely evening , while Hamish played "Auld lang Syne" they were able to join hands and sing the words.
Once again the Padre addressed the men, thanking all for making the evening so enjoyable and extending his thanks to the "Nightingale" of the evening, Skinny Liz.
Before we retire I will leave you with a few words of wisdom.......
I'm sure that many of you are familiar with the words of Omar Khayyam, that wise Persian sage who lived around the year 1020, it was quite difficult to find words of his to fit the occasion so I hope these will suit....
"There was a door to which I found no key,

There was a veil through which I could not see.
Some little talk of me and thee———————-
There was————- and then no more of thee and me.
And now let us pray...... God? Grant me the serenity to accept things I cannot change, courage to change the things I can, and the wisdom to know the difference. May God bless you this Yuletide and may each one of you have a peaceful day".
As he turned to walk away they all shouted "Don't forget to hang your stocking up".
Then all was quiet while Hamish played the National Anthem and the men sang the words.
"Come on lads, hang up your socks, and no smelly ones else you'll get nowt. Tomorrow morning each man should find he had a packet of cigarettes, tablet of soap, handkerchief or some useful little items left in the night by Santa Claus.
"Wonder what we'll get for dinner tomorrow"?
"Well there's one thing for sure, it won't be bully beef (corned beef) or tinned pork and bean".
Hewell Grange had its own farm and garden produce, they would be well provided for.....

RUDYARD KIPLING 1865 - 1936

TOMMY

I went into a theatre as sober as could be,
They gave a drunk civilian room, but 'adn't none for me,
They sent me to the gallery or round the music halls,
But when it come to fighting, Lord - they'll shove me in the stalls.

For it's Tommy this and Tommy that, an Tommy wait outside,
But it's special train for Atkins when the trooper's on the tide....
The troopships on the tide my boys, the troopships on the tide
Oh it's a special train for Atkins when the trooper's on the tide.

We aint no thin red 'eroes, nor we aint no blackguards too.
But single men in barracks, most remarkle like you.
An' if sometimes our conduct isn't all your fancy paints
Why single men in barricks don't grow into plaster saints.

While it's Tommy this and Tommy that and Tommy fall behind,
But it's please to walk in front, sir, when there's trouble in the wind,
Oh it's please to walk in front, sir, when there's trouble in the wind.

You talk O better food for us, and schools an fires an all.
We'll wait for extra rations if you treat us rational.
Don't mess about the cook room slops, but prove it to our face,
The Widows Uniform is not the soldiers mans disgrace.

For it's Tommy this and Tommy that and Tommy chuck him out the brute,
But it's Saviour of 'is country when the guns begin to shoot,
An it's Tommy this and Tommy that an anything' you please,
An Tommy ain't a blooming fool, you bet that Tommy sees.

CHAPTER SEVEN

Redditch Indicator
Wartime Memories 1914 - 1918

Christmas Eve at Tardebigge V. A. D. Hospital 1915

There were twenty six patients present this year. Presents included wollen gloves, pipes, trench mirrors (metal mirrors), photo cases, air cushions, tinder lighters and many useful little items.
During the day the hospital was visited by the Countess of Plymouth who presented each man with the gift of a razor. Messrs Cadbury & Co. also delivered boxes of chocolates, other generous donors sent turkey, ham, cigars, tobacco, cigarettes, pencil, writing outfits and silk handkerchiefs.
Once again Christmas memories of the hospital would live in the patients hearts for a very long time, as one lad remarked "That's some thing to take back to the trenches when we go!".
They would never forget breakfast at 9.00, dinner at 1.00, Tea at 5.00.
When "Cot time" (bedtime) arrived every "Tommy" felt he owed a debt of gratitude to the staff and to the numerous generous donors of presents.
How wonderful to think that these lads were never short of entertainment, there was always some voluntary organisation so willing to do their best for these men who had given so much.

Redditch Indicator Nov 27th 1915

On Sat Nov 20th Royal Antediluvian Order of Buffaloes gave a concert to entertain the wounded soldiers and sailors at the Tardebigge V. A. D. Hospital. It was a lengthy programme and very much enjoyed.
Many songs were sung, and most of them the lads could join in, they all loved a sing song, it helped them to forget their pain and sorrow. The concert consisted of light entertainment, comic turns and card tricks, short stories and the following songs.
Boys of the old brigade
The Battle Eve
Sunshine of your smile
The soldiers farewell
They built Piccadilly for me

The evening ended with Auld Lang Syne followed by God Save the Queen. The concert party was thanked by Miss Walford and this was followed by cups of tea and a rousing round of applause.

Christmas Day 1915

The V. A. D. hospital patients attended Holy Communion at Tardebigge Church. It was not far from the hall to the church, across the Pleck and into School Lane and they were there, very smart in their hospital blue suits with the white lining of the trouser leg turned up. They liked to walk for health reasons and often walked to Foxlydiate, village next to Hewell. After church they all sat down to breakfast at 9.00 a.m.

Each man received a little heap of presents beside his plate from the staff. Birmingham Mail Christmas tree Fund provided a pair of gloves, Messrs Cadbury sent chocolates.

They also received gifts from friends living in Bromsgrove, Redditch and surrounding districts. Private Aikman (K. O. S. B.) was responsible for table decoration at dinner and each patient received a small keepsake in his plum pudding. The Christmas tea table was festooned with crackers and the evening was spent playing musical chairs, once again the day ended with Auld Lang Syne and God Save The King.

A party of wounded soldiers and sailors were taken in cars from the V. A. D. Hospital to be entertained by the Earl & Countess of Plymouth at the Badminton Court, Barnt Green Close.

April 15th 1916

A parcel was delivered to the Tardebigge V. A. D. hospital from the Red Cross Redditch Depot containing,

Thirty one pairs ....Pyjamas
Fifty Three.........bed coats
NINE NIGHTINGALES
Thirty eight pairs of slippers
Fourteen pairs of mittens
Seven scarves and Four face cloths

A nightingale was a bed cloak made out of two yards of flannel, designed by FLORENCE NIGHTINGALE for soldiers in the Barrack hospital at Scutari who were wounded during the Crimea.

This garment was cut from one single piece of flannel.

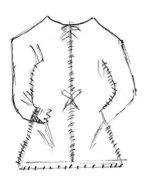

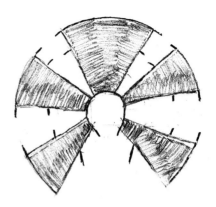

Nightingale Bed Cloak

Nightingale Pattern cut from 2yds Flannel

Saturday March 17th 1916......Redditch Indicator

On Saturday March 10th an orchestral concert was given at the V. A. D. Hospital Tardebigge by the Redditch Brotherhood, Band Conductor Mr. W. A. Dean.

Attended by forty wounded soldiers, instrumental selections included "Il Travatore, Presidents March, Cavelleria Rusticana, the Bacarolle, and Bohemian Girl". The songs that followed were, "Rose of my heart", and "If you were the only girl in the World" and many other songs well known to the lads, they always enjoyed a good sing song so all of these were highly appreciated.

The commandant on behalf of the soldiers thanked the conductor and his band.

November 16th 1916.........Redditch Indicator.

Bromsgrove and Redditch Red Cross Fund organised a sale and flag day, Target £1000.00 in aid of the Tardebigge V. A. D. Hospital and Red Cross Society.

The committee appealed for household goods, antiques and livestock. Other people mentioned for their help and generosity were Milwards of Redditch, Weaver and Guest, Grocers of Bromsgrove, Dr. and Mrs. Banks of Redditch.

Thursday 12th December ....Advertisement reads as follows.........

Scenes of the Somme Battlefield.

"GOODBYE OLD MAN"

The painting (pictured here) by J. Matania was commissioned in 1916 by the Blue Cross to raise money for the relief of suffering among war horses........

Permission to include this picture in this book was kindly given by the editor of "This England Journal".

THIS ENGLAND, Autumn, 1984

Inter Lantern Lecture.
In connection with the special appeal for £200.00 for the work of the Tardebigge V. A. D. Hospital a lecture will be given at the :
Redditch Temperance Hall on
Thursday Dec. 12th by,
The Rev. John. H. Brookes of Bromsgrove.
Entitled "Scenes of the Somme Battlefield".
Illustrated by a unique series of specially prepared lantern slides.
Chairman A. C. Millard J.P.
Tickets of admission 25/-........125 new pence or 300 old pennies.
Obtainable from Hodges - Stationers, Evesham Street, Redditch.
Doors open at 7.00 p.m. and commence at 7.30 p.m.
Saturday July 1st 1916
A party of wounded soldiers and sailors were taken in cars from the V. A. D. Hospital to be entertained by the Earl and Countess of Plymouth at the Badminton Court, Barnt Green close to the Lickey Hills.
Games and competitions and other amusements were enjoyed by all present.
A meeting was held at Hewell Grange by the R. S. P. C. A. to discuss ways to raise funds for helping the Army Veterinary Corps. to minimise the suffering of horses, mules and donkeys at the front line. Funds were desperately needed for sick and wounded animals.
A large assortment of selected vegetables were carefully packed and dispatched to the North Sea Fleet on November 15th 1916, all the produce came from Hewell Gardens.

The Soldier's Kiss

Only a dying horse, pull off the gear
And slip the needless bit from frothing jaws.
Drag it aside there, leave the roadway clear -
The battery thunders on with scarce a pause.

Prone by the shell swept highway, there it lies
With quivering limbs, as fast the life tide falls,
Dark films are closing o'er the faithful eyes
That mutely plead for aid where none avails.

Onward the battery rolls, but one there speeds
Heedless of comrades voice or bursting shell,

Back to the wounded friend who lonely bleeds
Beside the stoney highway where it fell.

Only a dying horse! He swiftly kneels,
Lifts the limp head and hears the shivering sigh
Kisses his friend, while down his cheek there steals
Sweet pirty's tear, "Goodbye, old man, goodbye".

No honour wait him, medal, badge or star,
Though scarce could war a kinder deed unfold,
He bears within his breast, more precious,
Far beyond the gift of Kings, A heart of gold.

HENRY CHAPPELL.

This description is of an actual incident on the road to a battery position in
southern Flanders.
Permission to include this poem was kindly given by the editor of "This
England Journal".
The following verses are from the Redditch Indicator Dec 21st 1916.

Christmas to Mother.

With brightest radiance glowed the star
A soft wind signed to cease.
In Marys waiting arms was laid
The Infant Prince of Peace.

The wise men knew, tho still afar
And haste had no surcease
Their gifts, thought Mary none to rare
For her sweet babe of Peace.

Yet as in strength and grace he grew,
She saw midst joys increase
His touch would end all strife and woe
Her blessed son of Peace.

While bowed beneath the Cross she stood
The dark hour brought release.

And set on high, with glory crowned
A Saviour of our Peace.

O' Christ child fill these empty arms
So sorrow shall decease
And Mary's bliss each mother know
Who gave her child for Peace.

W.M. Webb.

February 24th 1917.

The Price

What is the price of Victory Won
with reeling sword and murderous gun.
And horse for battle shod.
no fierce invading foes defile
Or stained with blood it's sod.

To Mothers go and sires who weep
And sons who lie where heroes sleep their lives of sacrifice.
Their tears flow fast by household fires,
In lonely homes, when day retires, go
Ask them of the price.

Go, ask the price that lover paid
When death at youth, blood portal slayed
And stole love's choicest gem.
Go to the mourning widow there with children round a vacant chair,
Go ask the price of them.

Redditch Alonza

Redditch Indicator   Dec 22nd 1917.

There was an old worker of Tardebigge
Who never made good tho so hard he'd dig,
He'd plough and he'd sow,
But he seldom could mow

And the only good thing was his pig.

Various little verse written by local poets appeared in the Redditch
Indicator following the Armistice

Yet none oh Lord have perfect rest,
For none are wholly free from sin.
And they who fain would serve thee best,
Are conscious most of wrong within.

And tho, the frost be keen
And tho, the nights be long,
I know that Spring will come again
And I'll sing my morning song.
Thus sings the Robin........
By invitation of Lady Plymouth. Hewell Grange.
The Women's Institute held a meeting to ask the members to canvas the
parish for volunteers for National Service.
There followed a demonstration for fruit bottling which was held in the
wood carving room, permission kindly granted by the Countess of
Plymouth.

Redditch Indicator - August 4th 1917 - My Bivouac

It's only some rag and canvas
Hitched on to a blooming tree,
There 'aint no name in the fanlight,
'Cos there 'aint no fanlight to see

It's a hasty knocked up shanty
Wiv branches, wire and string,
For it 'aint no back pack either
"The Limit" we call the thing.

I love me dear old "bivvy",
For what it's walls contain,
There's photos on the wall there
Of folks who at home remain.

On the floor fag ends are lying

To waste them would be a sin,
Tomorrow I'll have to smoke 'em,
With the aid of a safety pin.
Pioneer A. G. Joyner (of the Laurels Hopwood).
R. C. Coy. (338 Royal Engineers - B. E. F.)
British Expeditionary Force - France.

Christmas Day V. A. D. Hospital 1918

At 12.00 the patients sat down to a sumptuous dinner, following the signing of the Armistice this would be their last Christmas here.
At 5.00 p.m. Hospital staff, patients with their relatives and friends sat down together for tea. Captain Watford played Santa Claus and with and enormous "lump in his throat" gave a speech and paid tribute to everyone concerned. He then distributed presents to all from a very heavily laiden tree. The rest of the evening was spent with dancing, games and songs. The party finished with "Auld Lang Syne" followed by God Save the King.
Many of them knew that they would be returning abroad to war torn countries for policing and administration work. They never forgot the care and hospitality they had received during their stay in Tardebigge.

1916 The New Year was let in by a Private from the Royal Berkshire Regiment who carried in the hospital mascot, a black cat. At 12.30 a.m. a New Year concert was provided by Miss Milward attended by all the patient and staff who showed full appreciation of all the items included.

CHAPTER EIGHT

1917 Passchendaele and other stories.

Once again the V. A. D. Hospital made preparations for a new intake of soldiers and sailors. How wonderful it was to be tucked up in clean white sheets. Many told the tales of how, until they had been taken to the field hospitals they had not washed their faces for fourteen days, some were carried in and even the hospitals staff shrank with horror to see what appeared to be a bundle of dirty old rags, smelling foul and stiff with layer upon layer of thick mud which would later reveal, almost alive, a human being.

From field hospital to de - lousing stations from casualty clearing stations. Operating theatres were often spoken of as "slaughter houses". Patients were labelled P. U. O. (Pyrexia of unkown Origin).

Red labels - Haemorrhage

Cases for Blighty travelling by boat B.S. Boat sitting, B.L. Boat lying.

Cot cases - Shellshock, Hospital centres labelled A B (abdominals) Chests and femurs, Advanced abdominals, Burns and many, many others too numerous to mention.

Weeks on end the soldiers had forced their weary bodies through a quagmire of mud waist high, horses, mules and donkeys stared at the desperate men around, their searching eyes asking the same question over and over again, What had they done to deserve this?

The men had stood and gazed in horror as villages and farmlands turned into flat seas of mud, they watched helplessly as Passchendaele was obliterated.

They had lived for months in trenches, living like moles in underground tunnels where the atmosphere was so foul that even a candle wouldn't burn. They had also witnessed comrades tied to a post, blindfolded, and shot for desertion and cowardice. Now at last.......

This is one place in England where you can truly say............

God's in his heaven, all's right with the world.

To breathe the clear fresh English country air was an experience long forgotten.

Red sky in the Morning, was truly, shepherds warning (no longer Jerry's warning). Red sky at night, really meant shepherd delight (no longer Jerry's delight).

After the patients had settled in there were the usual questions to be answered, "Who's the older lady then, is she the boss?"

"She's not old, she is in charge and is the Commandant".

"Well she looks old, older than the nurses, my dad always says. A woman is as old as she looks and a man's old when he's stopped looking".

Most of the patients were awake early next day. They were never short of visitors. Lady Plymouth was a regular visitor and extremely good for the patients morale, especially those confined to bed or bathchair. Sitting up in beds covered in white counterpanes wearing their Nightingale bed jackets they all looked very smart. Often they would hold their tobacco pipes in their hands, often unlit, they would refer to them as their "comforter" and just for that present moment in time in spite of their pain and injuries they looked at peace with the world. The sun streaming in casting it's shadows round the ward, known to the country folk as "St . Lukes Little Summer".

"Just the day for a walk down an English country lane and pick some blackberries, any one fancy a walk?"

"Not me" remarked one sleepy head, "Gosh I feel like death warmed up".

"Better get going if you want to find blackberries, the "Devil" will soon be along to put his feet on them and they will loose their flavour".

This saying comes from when the first frosts cause a bloom on the berries. The sun had vanished behind a cloud and someone said "It's as black as the Ace of Spades over Bill's mother's way". (Country saying).

The boys in blue, as they were known to the village, liked to walk down to Tardebigge Tunnel and talk to the canal workmen, often they would get a

ride on the tug, they loved to sing when they were in the darkest part, war time songs....but...I'm afraid their versions have been censored...so sorry....not for publication.....

One young lad was proud of the fact that he had been able to hang on to his ammunition pouch. "But that's a school satchel" remarked a nurse not aware that all school satchels were requisitioned for that particular use.

There was a lot of talk about Princess Mary's fund, one of the principal charities to supply a Christmas gift for anyone wearing King's uniform. Many of them treasured the Christmas card they had received from the King and Queen.

The Great War...

The First World War..........Ironically....a.....

War to end Wars .. or so it was called !!!!

It is now eighty years since the Battle of Passchendaele and there are men alive today who can still recall the horrors of 1917.

The battle was raging from July to November during which time it rained and it rained, only Noah had seen it rain like this. As far as the eye could see everywhere was a deep sea of liquid mud.

All the artillery was sucked into the mud, gun carriages went down, horses and mules with them.

Wounded men disappeared and were beyond help.

The winter of 1917 was the worst winter of the war.

Many old soldiers have outstanding recollections of the courage of ordinary lads. It was in 1917 that another sinister unknown virus raised it's ugly head. Europe was hit by an epidemic known as "Spanish Flu" and many undertakers were unable to cope, bodies decomposed rapidly, the death rate was higher than the figures shown for the war years.

Two of my sisters died during this appalling epidemic.

Iodine, Eusol Solution, Peroxide, Lysol were all antiseptics for cleaning wounds. Frost bitten feet and hands were wrapped in cotton wool, lint and oiled silk.

Trench fever was thought to be caused by lice.

Often the men would sit in their dugouts and hold a lighted match to the seams of their rough khaki uniforms, as one soldier remarked, "I was hoping to roast the little blighters alive, as for the nurses, God Bless Them, them poor dears, used to comb out their long hair to see how many they could catch, they used to call them "greybacks" and believe me, some of those lousy lice were quite big".

Iadoform, Bicarbonate of soda, Linseed for a poultice, Morphia injections for pain, Quinine, Arrowroot, splints were made of paper mache and as the war

V.A.D.'s and Patients 1914 - 1918, Tardebigge V.A.D. Hospital

dragged on many of these items were now in short supply. There were many other medicines and lotions too numerous to mention.

The biggest headache of all was the appalling number of cases of Gas Gangrene, little was known about this infection, caused by the Anaerobic micro-organism which grows and lives where there is no free oxygen. Wounds blew up like hollow balloons filled with gas and rotting tissue, it had no connection with the poison gas used in the war.

Some optimistic souls said "The war will be over for Christmas" but they forgot to say......Which Christmas?...........

As the months rolled by people on the Home Front struggled to keep things moving, collections of blankets and bed linen continued. Horses and carts travelled around the streets from dawn till dusk gathering up any small item of scrap iron that could be used towards making ammunition.

Meanwhile, knitting and sewing for the troops continued and Punch Magazine continued with it's humourous war cartoons. Elderly genteel ladies combed every long haired dog they could lay their hands on and owners of spinning wheels spun the softest wool that was ever used. It was then knitted into small blankets for bathchair patients or little capes to go round their shoulders.

Once patient recalls how he was sent the most beautiful pair of hand

Hewell Fields, Redditch - Maurice Clarke Collection

knitted socks which quickly found their way onto his ice cold feet, his mate replied "That'll keep the frost bite away".

Ten days later when those feet and socks had covered many miles he wondered why the toes on one foot were very, very sore so he removed his sock, placed his hand inside to turn the sock inside out and as he did a small piece of folded cardboard fell onto the mud. "Well I never", he declared, "Someone's sent me a love letter". He read the following message and his eyes filled with tears.

Dear Boy,

"Whoever you are and wherever you may be, you will always be in my prayers, I know I will never see my grandsons again, but I will think of my unknown soldier. God keep you in his care".

From one who thinks about you.

"Dear old lady" he muttered aloud to which his mate replied, "A good job she couldn't hear what you said about her socks, but then you were not to know she had smuggled a note in the toe".

There were quite a few young lads in this new intake of patients, amongst their many injuries some had Synovitis of the knees, also referred to by the troops as.."Sign of Blighty Knee" which made walking so painful it was enough to get a transfer to a hospital nearer home.

"Can I call you Miss Nurse" one patient enquired, "And is the older lady Matron?" "No came the reply", she is the Commandant.

"Oh, so what does V. A. D. stand for?. "It means Voluntary Aid Detachment". "She, looks to me like, um, like er, er a Very Awful Dragon, please don't tell her I said so!..

After tea the lads would gather round and try to remember some of the funny stories they had heard.

One soldier told of an experience that he would never have dreamed about....as he put it...."Never in my wildest dreams".

"It was a still night, a full moon shone down like a huge silver ball, I sat there outside the dugout, (a shelter dug in the ground), thinking to myself, I wonder what the enemy is cooking up now, it's too quiet to be comfortable, I think I'll risk it and rub some whale oil on my poor old feet".

The only sound was the quiet eerie whistle as the enemy fired by pistol coloured Very lights (flares) into the still night otherwise it was as silent as the grave, suddenly the most beautiful sound that I ever heard broke the silence, it was a nightingale singing and I have never heard one sing like that before. Amidst all the mud, blood and mangled bodies the sound was so poignant that it made the tears roll down my cheeks".

The other patients just sat there spellbound and no one spoke a word.

"One of the most amusing stories I recall", remarked a patient "Was a lad, a signaller, he was instructed to deliver a basket of carrier pigeons to prepare them for their long flights with coded messages, when he arrived back at he station he was greeted by the corporal who roared "Where the.......... have you been, thought you must have returned to Blighty, where are the pigeons?".

"Well" the lad replied, "I feathered those and cooked them, me and me mate shared them, we're fed up with bully beef, pork and beans". The corporal was shaking with fury and I never did find out what happened to the

1914 - 1918 Troops H.M.V. Gramaphone

culprit, he could have been let off lightly......

Dogs were also trained to carry messages.

The men talked abut the Angels of Mons (1914) and the White Cavalry (1918), there had been many stories passed down the lines relating to the wonderful "Beings" that had appeared with upstretched arms placing themselves between the Tommies and the enemy. Apparitions in white robes with bare heads appeared on a day of National Prayer, There was much talk about these weird and wonderful things and many of the men present were keen to pursue these stories later on in life.

Now amongst this group of patients were three Scots and four sailors, they had all sailed back to Blighty together. Ben, one of the sailors was anxious to tell the story of how a certain Scotsman on boarding has missed his footing and landed in the ice cold sea.

Poor man, too bashful to remove his kilt, he stood back from his comrades while water from seven yards of material flowed down his legs making a huge pool of the floor.

Also on board a group of V.A. D's, were wondering what they could do to help, suddenly one of the nurses from the back of the group walked across and said to the poor bedraggled man "Come on laddie, no time for modesty, put these on".

Without a blush she handed him a pair of ladies silk bloomers (often referred to as "directroire knickers) without a word the Scotsman stepped into the garment, the legs were long and threaded with elastic there were shouts of "You look as though you've got your "Knee Breeches on Jock" and other rude remarks.

This story caused much laughter from the patients followed by "Was it you Mac?, hope the nurse didn't catch a cold, What about you Willie, you're very quiet and you Hamish, where were you when this was going on?" But Hamish only smiled............So the question remains unanswered........Who did go back to Blighty in Nurse's Knickers?............

But the night was still young and the men continued to reminisce, suddenly one young man said,

"Does any one here have any recollections about the first Christmas of the War?"

"Well laddie it depends on what you have in mind, what I've got on my mind this moment wouldn't be fit for these ears around here!!!"

"Well", the lad replied, "I was thinking about that night in the trenches in No Man's Land, we were so close to the enemy and singing all the carols that came to mind, trying to forget the mud, utter desolation, the rats and the lice, when suddenly out of the eerie stillness came the sound of the beautiful carol "Stille Nacht, Heilige Nacht", it was played on a gramophone, brought tears to the eyes of many men, I know I will never forgot it, dear God, when you think about it, there we were blowing each other's heads off one minute and the next singing that lovely Austrian Carol, the Germans in their language and the British Tommy in his, doesn't make sense does it". the lad paused and wiped the tears away and to "break the ice" someone said "I'll tell you the story of Silent Night, Holy Night, we owe it to two young Austrian men and a mouse. About one hundred years ago a little mouse found himself a lovely little home in the pipes of a church organ near Saltzburg this little mouse discovered a very tasty morsel to nibble.... lovely soft leather from the organ bellows, it almost put the "tin hat" on the Christmas Eve service. Now the priest was very worried but he was a gifted man, so with his words and his friend the church organist, who was a gifted musician, between the two and the choir of the school children Silent Night was born.

Naturally it didn't please everyone, many were displeased at hearing a guitar played in church, such a thing had never been heard of, so the music lay forgotten in the church cupboard until it was finally heard by the man who came to repair the organ. He was quite amused by the story of the little mouse and asked if he might take the music to show some friends, who I believe were a group of singers.

They were so impressed and their performance was heard by a German

Broke as you are, I
love you.

publisher and eventually the carol became know all over Europe. Sad to think that the priest who had written the words died before he became well known but every year a local choir stands by his grave and the lively strains of Silent Night can be heard drifting across the still cold air. Let me just tell you that the Christmas that our young friend talks about when the English and Germans sang that carol silenced the guns for a while and this is where the saying came from "All quiet on the Western Front".

Now it's time we were all quiet so come on lads into your cots and a good nights sleep for all, Oh, and don't forget the next time you sing Silent Night spare a thought for the hungry little mouse............

I was fortunate to know two members of the R.A.M.C. (Royal Army Medical Corps). They had worked in the Field Hospitals where the only lighting provided was candlelight. There was nothing that they could ever see or hear in future years that would ever shake them because in simple words......they had seen it and heard it all.

One of the blessings was, (only a minor detail, but it was invaluable) that Tetanus Anti Toxin was widely used and prevented many fatalities. Sadly, there was no cure available to treat Gas Gangrene, one of the major headaches of all medical personnel.

"Ah", said one, "It was a heartache too, looking on and watching as they slipped through our fingers and there was nothing we could do about it".

Gas Gangrene was often referred to as "bacillus welch"!! or B.Welchi named after W. Henry Welch who discovered the micro-organisms most commonly found in agricultural land, the battlefields of Flanders and elsewhere were ideal breeding grounds.

They suggested that in many ways fate had been kind to them, they did not realize that when they related their stories back home and spoke of meeting and working in the same hospital as Alexander Fleming, they would later on in life be treated with his life saving wonder drug, Penicillin.

They had in their own words "rubbed shoulders with Sir Almoth Wright who was responsible for the Typhoid Fever vaccine.

The American surgeon Harvey Cushing, well known in the field of Neurosurgery.

One story stood out very vividly, it told of a surgeon who on writing to his relatives back home stated... I am well able to cope with the mud, the rats and the lice, supplies which are short and many other items... what I cannot cope with are the holes in my socks........

I was just about to thank them for their war time memories and leave them alone with their thoughts. They had served their country well these two brothers and I knew that I would meet them again. It was a homely picture, there they were sitting one either side of the fire place. A lovely fire throwing it's warmth out across the living room, puffing away at their pipes they looked at peace with the world.

They had never married, this had been their childhood home and they did not intend to leave.

Just as I was putting my hand on the door knob Ben called out.

"Syd's just remembered something else, come on Syd she knows you're a bit shy, tell her".

Oh good I thought, another story, well my time is my own, but I added "I can't stay for tea today".

"Well nurse you'll be interested in this one, I was given orders to report to the big hospital at Roehampton, I wasn't sorry, I'd had a few rough crossing back and forth across the Channel, some of the big Casinos in Paris had become hospitals, Neuilly was the headquarters for the American Field Ambulance Service and I had been there. I welcomed a spot of duty back in dear old Blighty but, I wasn't quite prepared for the scenes at Roehampton. "Poor chaps, no wonder they called them "The Faceless ones" I must admit, I'd seen so many shattered limbs. I suppose I hadn't given much thought to jaws, ears and noses, I can only describe the work of re-building these fragmented features as miraculous. It was weird to enter into these rooms at night and to know that you were being watched by rows of silent white faces, masks made out of Plaster of Paris. The men had many names for these units, one that sticks in my mind is....The Ghouldy Goblin's Garden.... and many of the lads spoke of a book written by a French author in 1911 "Phantome de L'Opera".

My brother and myself went to see Lon Chany in the film when it came out at the end of the 1920's. We had many thoughts in our mind that other folk in this picute house wouldn't have dreamt of!!! By gosh, those surgeons did some wonderful work and many of those men who were carried into the field hospitals without a face are still alive today (1945 - 1950).

"But you know nurse, this was the start of the work on skin and bones, a special hospital was set up in London before the end of the war, it was a dream of the future, Plastic Surgery, I would have loved to have been in the background, never the less I've seen many horrors and also some very wonderful things".

As I left I thought to myself, what a story, if ever this was told it's going to take a bit or sorting out from my little notes, but you never know I might get around to using them....one day....we'll see.

Author's note.....

Paris Opera House, built by Charles Gunier 1861 - 1875
Employed 1500 workers and kept it's own stable of white horses.
The book "Phantome de L'Opera" 1911 was based on strange events which occurred in this famous building in the 1880's.
The Paris Opera rose to it's fame after the French Revolution when it was restored by Napoleon in the reforms of 1807.

"Don't anyone dare to tell grisly stories, instead think about all the rum rations you've just had, just let anybody say to me...." Over the top with the best of luck, because we have all been over the top, and I can assure them it wasn't with the best of luck.....

"Mind you it's grand to have a real cup of good tea".

Often the water available at the front was brackish (salty and nauseating), it was collected at night and it was anyone's guess as to what had been floating in it!!

Chlorination tablets were used to kill germs. These tablets would also remove the rust from parts of horses harness. They would also clean leather and boots, as one patient said "Gawd knows what they did to my guts......".

There were many, many men who would never work again, many funds were set up to raise money to assist them.

Outstanding recollections became every day words as people spoke of the courage of ordinary lads.

The Poppy became the symbol for the annual appeal, hundreds of thousands grew in Flanders' Fields on the Western Front and so November 11th became Remembrance Day.

Each year we wear our poppies with pride, still made by ex-servicemen and

so the poppies of Flanders live on to remind us that Every serving man or
woman was a HERO..........
"Did someone call?", the poppy said
The corn bowed down it's golden head
Poppies growing straight and tall
Knowing they are loved by all.

A gentle swaying of the breeze,
Leaves whispering in the trees,
The poppies shed their petals red
Falling on a soldiers bed.

The silent snowflakes falling down
Change the colour of the ground,
Tread softly for the dead are sleeping
Only the birds can hear you weeping.

Written by the author.................

The Trumpeter by Airlie Dix

2nd verse
Tread light or the dead in the valley
They are lying around face down to the ground,
And they can't hear me sound the reveille,
I'm calling them home, come home.

Sung by John Mc Cormack, recorded by H.M.V. Circa 1920
This well known Irish Tenor later became Count John Mc Cormack.

CHAPTER NINE

Soldier to Socials

At the end of 1918 and the following year the enormous task of reverting back to peace conditions began.

Amongst tearful and grateful goodbyes the Soldiers and Sailors left the V.A. D. Hospital for the last time, many to return to civilian life, others would return to France and other war torn areas to help with the mammoth task of clearing up and getting the countries back on their feet again.

Every local serving man was presented with a Silver Cigarette case inscribed with his name.

Slowly village life became alive again. Whilst drives and dances were held in the school room, confirmation was held. The vicar of Tardebigge was the Rev. F. G. Ellerton. The girls' veils were given and made by the needlework guild.

It was at this time that the Tardebigge Needlework Guild closed it's labour's, the work began in 1914 and met at fortnightly intervals without a break, it helped equip the V.A. D. Hospital with various items.

Over 1000 garments, mainly shirts and pyjamas were sent to the various depots. It supplied our own serving men and sent them Christmas presents of shirts and socks.

In the early days of the war the Belgians were also provided with clothing, members of the working party raised money for material which amounted to £176.00 old money, material was also donated and as the meeting closed there was a sum of £7. 6. 2d (old money).

Once again the village boys set to work to restore the old hall back to it's natural splendour. On their knees they waxed and polished until once again the floors were returned to their original state.

White lines were again painted to mark out the floors for Badminton. The weaving shed at the back of the Hall for the last four years had been used as a soup kitchen, no longer would it be necessary for the lads to stand and queue with their milkcans waiting for 6 pence (old money) worth of soup.

Preparations could now go ahead for future social gatherings. There would be dancing agin on a Saturday night, many a lad would find a lass somewhere on the dance floor, picking up the steps again, dances like the Veleta, Military Two Step and the good old fashioned Gay Gordons were always popular, male partners were in short supply but many of the dances would get everyone up on the floor.

Dances were held by Hewell Cricket Club and Tennis Clubs, there were post war concerts and pantomimes, all of which were well supported. Booking for the use of the Hall were so advanced it was often a problem to arrange future events.

Arrangements were made well in advance of May 1937 for the Coronation of King George VI and Queen Elizabeth, such a happy event, even the weather was kind to us.

Flags and bunting flew everywhere, church bells rang out their joyous peels to welcome the New King and Queen.

Hewell Park was overflowing with so many happy people, the Village Hall was used for refreshments and entertainment during the evening.

On December 28th 1937 Hewell Cricket Club held a well attended Dinner Dance with more than eighty people present. Music was provided by those well known local musicians Horace and Sydney Beszant and spot prizes were won by local people from Redditch. The Beszant band was influenced by the music of the "Big Bands" of the 1940's, Benny Goodman, Artie Shaw, Glenn Miller, Tommy Dorsey and others.

Alas, how many people could look to the future and foretell what was in store, not many....

Once again, twenty one years after the signing of the Armistice at the end of the Great War....(A war to end wars)....War clouds were gathering once again and Great Britain was once again at war.

I had only just left school, as soon as I was able I became a St. John Ambulance Nursing Cadet until I reached the age to become a student nurse.

This was the moment that I had waited for, now so many dreams would come true........

During my early years there was so much talk about the Hewell Nursing Association. I heard many things, I wasn't supposed to hear. Often little whispers from people calling at the house, they were not to know that young Pat was hiding behind the hedge....

You know old Mrs. So and So well, er daughters just had another....and I heard tell this un'll live, well you knows...them others was un'ealthy...wonder if the bloke 'll marry her...this time...

All Greek to me...this but...carry on, Pat you might learn a little!!

You know old Mrs. Whatsit...well they sez it'll never get better, mind you...it'll get bigger, drop off one of these fine days.

I sees the nus goin in to ole Mrs. Oojar, she only sez it don't get any smaller. It must be bad cus er takes er little black bag in with her ... wonder if they be thinkin about takin it out... er'll miss it when it's gone...

Hadn't better say too much just in case Pat's around.

Oh, look out here's Mrs Thingy....come for your money again, ave ya, still you never know might be glad of the "NUS" one day.....still twopence is it? (old money), don't know if I can afford twopence this week...you never know...might want the nus meself one day...

At this point a great cackle of laughter rang rang through to air....as long as er dusn't, bring her little black bag I shan't mind....

Hadn't better say too much if young Pat's around might wet er appetite a bit more for nursin...

Well, what an entertaining time I've had.

They try very hard but they will not make me change my mind....

I will still be a nurse.... One day....

The following pages are extracts taken from the exact minutes of the monthly meetings which were held in connection with the Tardebigge District Nursing Association from January 1930 until it was disbanded in September 1946, prior to the commencement of The National Health Service.

Throughout, the years of service which the Association gave the Officers and Committee consisted of the landowners of the parish, business men and women and the vicar. During the latter years the Countess of Plymouth was elected President. I notice that throughout the book the three most used words are "It was decided". I am grateful to my colleague District Nurse Caroline Hirons for the loan of the book.

I remember my father telling me about these meetings also his words of wisdom "Be warned my wench, never get mixed up with them their committee meetings, you won't know if you be on foot or horse back by the time they have finished with you, what do you want to give up a good job for to go nursing? You are earning 7/6d (old money) a week. When you become a student nurse you'll get 18/11d (old money) a month, you won't have enough to pay your bus fare home if you get a day off". But I must find out these things for myself and there is only one way - the hard way...

As far back as I could remember there was always talk in the house, at the bus stops, in the shops, indeed wherever I went it was always the topic of conversation, "Havin' in the Nus' and the Hewell Nursing Association were everyday household words, where the 'Nus' had bin and what she done an' why, don't want your Pat to 'ear ole Mrs So and So...you knows...er bin laid out...Ooh is er dead then?....

The Hewell Nursing Association was formed in 1894 to provide resident nurses at a low fee to regular subscribers. This entitled any member of the family to be nursed in their own home. It was decided to form a Tardebigge District Nursing Association. An open meeting was held in Tardebigge Village Hall on December 12th 1929, the chair was taken by Lady Irene, Countess of Plymouth. Anyone willing to join to pay a contribution of two pennies a week, this would entitle the contributor to the services of the District Nurse. A committee was set up there and then with a committee meeting to be held monthly. Quarter days were March 26th, Lady Day, June 24th Midsummer, September 29th Michelmas and December 25th Christmas. At the first meeting the Chairman stated that the hospital gave 1/- a visit for cases where the patient was a contributor if certified by a doctor.

It was decided to circularize all medical men in the area informing them of the formation of the Association and asking them for their co-operation and sympathy. The rules of the County Association and of The Queen Victoria Institute were then considered and it was decided to apply for affiliation to the Institute and to accept the County Association rules with some modification. It was decided to charge 2d (old money) a week to contributors the fee to cover, husband, wife and children.

Anyone else living in the house to pay a separate contribution. Also, to invite subscriptions of 10/- (old money) and upwards. It was decided to ask for voluntary helpers to collect contribution. The rules were considered maternity fees were settled at 21/- (old money) to 42/- (old money) according to circumstances 42/- (old money) for non members. All members entitled to the free services of the nurse, non members to pay 2/6 (old money) first visit, and 1/- (old money) per visit afterwards. Sympathetic replies had been received from Doctors, two of them offering subscriptions. It was decided to procure a cupboard and the necessary books.

A District Nurse was appointed in January 1930, salary £180 p.a. to include board, lodging, laundry and uniform, and a rather heavy sit up and beg bicycle! The Nurse was introduced to the committee and asked to attend each month to give a detailed report of her work. It was decided to leave to Nurse discretion whether dressings should be paid for by the patient or the Association. The area should consist of Tardebigge Parish and part of Cobley Hill. Cases beyond this area were accepted within reason.

A bicycle was given to the Association for the benefit of the Nurse and the committee approved the expenditure of repairs to the same. It was hoped to receive a grant from the Birmingham Hospital Contributory Scheme but a letter from the secretary stated that no payments could be made by the scheme since a charge was made to members of the Association. It was then decided when Nurse should have her holiday and it was provisionally decided that this should take place in October !! The nurse then gave her report which convinced the committee that she was paying approximately 300 visits per month!! It was decided to hold a monthly meeting of the Executive committee, a quarterly meeting of the collectors and a General Meeting annually. The question of old people living in a household was considered, it was decided to include one person and to consider others as the cases arose.

In order to facilitate co-operation with the Hewell Nursing Association it was decided that subscribers to the Hewell Association shall have the services of the Tardebigge Association District Nurse of 6d (old money) per visit instead of 1/- (old money) if they are non-subscribers to the Tardebigge Association in general illness and in maternity cases for 35/- (old money). A report of inspection was read to the committee from the Queens District Nursing Association stating that the nurse's work was satisfactory and the Committee was satisfied that they to were "getting their pound of flesh"!!! It was decided to hold a Whist drive and Social. The nurse lived in rented rooms and a letter was read to the committee asking that arrangements be made concerning the rent of the rooms during the nurse's holiday. It was decided that the committee approved the nurse's arrangement of paying 5/- (old money) per week to hold her rooms during her annual leave.

There was still some misunderstanding regarding a merger between Tardebigge Association and Hewell Association. It was now quite obvious that they preffered to remain independent bodies. The treasurer reported that the Social had been a great success and had brought in between £12 and £13 (old money). A new nurse was to be appointed and it was decided that she was to have rooms at Plymouth House. Still hoping to provide the nurse with a car. It was also decided that the District Nurse does not perform the last offices to the dead unless by special request when the subscriber pays a minimum fee of 10/6d (old money) also there will be No Sunday Visits!! It was agreed to order a maternity bag to belong to the Association.

At the A.G.M. the treasurer stated in his report that the balance sheet showed a balance of £21 (old money) which proved that it had been a most successful year. A letter was received asking if Barnt Green could become part of the district and if so, it would be necessary to think about providing the nurse with a car! It was decided to approve the cost of repairs to the Nurse's bicycle which must be well maintained!! Repairs and spare parts are well under 10/- (old money) but a new bicycle will cost £3 (old money). Some problem has arisen regarding the resignation of the present nurse, a replacement has been recommended but the committee feel that the proposed nurse age 50 is too old! It was hoped to provide Nurse with a car. Nurse has asked the committee for permission to change her rooms as she was not comfortable at Plymouth House. After considerable discussion <u>it was decided</u> that although Nurse's comfort was the main consideration the committee would be sorry if she did move. The decision was that the nurse should suggest a little more care and consideration for her, but if this was not forthcoming, then she had their permission to move but it was clearly stated that Nurse must make her own arrangements. Nurse has asked for a new saddle for her bicycle but the committee must first approach "Terry's Spring Co."

<u>It was decided</u> that nurse should bring her notes along to each meeting to make sure that they were signed each month. The question of a car has arisen again. The question was raised regarding some of the very dilatory collectors, could they not be made to understand how badly they hampered the Associations work by their casual way of collecting subscriptions! <u>It was decided</u> that the vicar should speak personally to them. It was agreed that if subscribers lapsed in their payments that before they could avail themselves of the Nurse's service they must pay the last quarters subscriptions!!

Matter of the car postponed indefinitely...............

A nice shawl was presented to the Association to raffle. Would collectors sell tickets at 3d each, but the matter was still under discussion regarding the way in which some of the collectors did their work. It made the Treasurer's accounts a very difficult matter and it was suggested they should be pulled up and told to mend their ways!!

Had the committee considered the question of change of means of transport? Nurse had now been on the district 12 months, it was pointed out that a bicycle well served the size of the area as this had been a crucial year in the Association it would not be considered advisable to embark on any further big expenses.

The District Nurse has informed the committee that she has decided to purchase a motor-cycle and what help can she expect regarding expenses? A long drawn out discussion took place and <u>it was decided</u> to offer her £5 per year expenses the Association to pay the tax and comprehensive policy, it was also pointed out to Nurse she would be using the machine for her own pleasure and amusement!

A discussion took place regarding the cases of real hardship in need of attendance and <u>it was decided</u> to give free attendance in illness. The Nurse has been involved in an accident whilst riding her motor-cycle. Following a long period of sick leave she has decided to resign. The new Nurse has informed the committee that she finds the existing bicycle very heavy so <u>it was decided</u> to approach The Royal Enfield Factory to see if they can supply a second hand cycle. A new one was later offered for £2. 2s 0d (old money). It was suggested that as Mrs X had not collected from her patch for so long a new collector be appointed. The A.G.M. stated that 1933 had been a difficult year. One Nurse had been involved in an accident. Her replacement had been taken ill, but someone off the Parish stepped into the breach and soldiered on. Some of the meetings were poorly attended, some members never attended at all, these should be weeded out. Almost each year is recorded as being a difficult year, but by 1944 the collectors are spoken of as being "the backbone of the society".

It was agreed that a letter should be printed and sent round to all people in the district who were not already subscribers to the T.N.D.A. pointing out the wonderful work done by the Nurse and the great need for funds...............

A meeting was called at the request of the Midland District Nursing Co-ordination Committee. This committee requested that all local committees to study the report and scheme and send their opinions as soon as possible. A representative had been chosen by Worcester for this co-ordination committee. The secretary began by reading the report but before she got to the scheme, a member rose from her seat and said it was all too difficult to understand and she considered it useless for the secretary to continue to read it out! After a long discussion <u>it was decided</u> to write to Worcester, and ask if it would be possible for them to send someone along and explain to them in simple language exactly what it means!!

It is reported that the work has increased again, and at times, Nurse has been very hard put to it, to carry on, she must leave her convalescent cases and give her attention to maternity and sick. The Birches Maternity Home has closed owing to lack of staff and Nurse will hardly know which way to turn during the next few weeks. To add to our problems orders from Worcester state, that each Nurse must have a months holiday per year, supply nurses will be available and next door nurses must take on each other's district. We will arrange for the nurses to take a fortnight twice yearly. A large increase in Nurse's salary has been ordered by Worcester so we will have to find more money than ever before, so a rummage sale has been suggested which should be devoted to the nursing. As this committee has now been running for 14 years, one or two thought it might be a good idea to resign and let in some new blood!!!

The secretary of the City and County of Worcester Nursing Association congratulated Tardebigge on it's progress, she also pointed out that as Nurse had to cycle round, she was not always fit to perform her work. She expressed hope that Tardebigge would soon find a way to providing a small car for Nurse's use.

A special meeting was called on June 6th 1935 re: the question of a car for the Nurse. After a long discussion it was announced that a member of the Committee had already bought the car in question. The collectors reported that the result of the canvas which would bring in about £10 (old money). A long discussion followed and the following resolution was passed:-

The Association regretted that it could not undertake the financial responsibility of a car and the donation was left with the Committee member to deal with as she thought fit. The Committee have appealed for a new nursing bag and someone has kindly presented one. A social was suggested the proceeds to go to the Nurse's car.

In 1936 a new Midwives Act was passed which would help local finances and local organisations had already been informed that nurse's salaries must be raised in proportion to their line of service. The Association must prove to the County Council that they had done their best to raise as much as possible, there would also be a car grant of £30 p.a. (old money).

An outstanding event took place in 1938 , the County Council reorganised it's boundaries. Webheath was removed from Tardebigge and part of Finstall Parish between Tutnall and the railway was added to it. It was stated that this re-organisation was forced upon Bromsgrove and Tardebigge and ignored the old unities of life within the Parishes, they considered only the effective working of a nursing district.

It has now been decided that anyone who has reached the age of 70 years may have the services of the nurse FREE.

It appears that throughout this book of minutes, Nurse's salaries vary. In 1930 she begins with £180 p.a. and in 1933 £178-16s-00d, 1936 £178-6s-6d. Proposed in 1942, that because of wartime conditions, Nurse's salary be raised to £175 per year, plus a £8-6s-0d War bonus.

One of the nurses was involved in a car accident. This must have been a real headache for the committee, it involved pages of writing relating to solicitors, County Courts, repairs to the old car, deposit loss of unsatisfactory car, cost of the court case, who said what happened and where and so it goes on and on. By 1943 the War Bonus had risen to £17 - 10s - 0d. It was decided that instead of giving nurse a rise in salary and so increasing her income tax, it would be better to give her help with her car insurance.

The secretary reported that a Mrs X had come into the district to live, joined the Association, had a baby and then ceased to pay her subscriptions. What it really amounted to, was that she had, had her baby for 4/4d!! It would be a good idea if the secretary wrote to her reminding her of these benefits, after all, nurse had given her particular care and attention. Her children are young and you never know, she may need Nurse's help again in the future. The Secretary received a letter from a certain gentleman, stating that as his mother was a subscriber to the Tardebigge Association he presumed she was entitled to the services of the District Nurse when she was living in the other areas.

The work of the District Nurse was very dear to the Countess of Plymouth's heart and it was thanks to the President's interest in Nurse's comfort that the Association was allowed a cottage on the Hewell estate and Nurse was very happy in her own little house.

The Rowney Green Shakespearian Society gave a performance of 'A Midsummer's Night Dream' in Hewell Park. Tickets were 3/- (old money), 2/- and 1/-. The play was a great success and brought in the sum of £8 (old money). A Whist Drive was held which raised the sum of £12 (old money). At the A.G.M., it was suggested that better means of transport be made available as the less exercise spent in getting from place to place the more efficient the nursing would be! The annual receipt and payment account shows cash in the hand to be 12/- (old money).

Petrol allowance for Nurse for three months £1-16s-0d (old money). It was proposed and seconded that Nurse be allowed two gallons of petrol weekly. It is nice to report that the bicycle which Nurse found to be so uncomfortable, has been purchased by a member of the Committee for the sum of £2 (old money). The district nurse's resignation was reported with regret but a nurse outside our boundary line has undertaken to fill the gap at a salary of £2 (old money) weekly. The Secretary was sorry to report that after much correspondence interviews and time, the nurse had changed her mind.

The Honourary Secretary from the Hanbury nursing Association has informed Tardebigge about Hanbury's merger with Bentley and states that they are faced with a problem, they cannot count on the car which was ordered some months ago being ready after the date fixed for amalgamation. Would someone in the Parish be willing to drive the nurse around? It was reported that nurse was using her slack period to do house to house visiting with great success.

It was difficult to imagine how the welfare of Tardebigge existed before the Association was formed. One wonders how this side of our life was covered without the district nurse. There were and always would be lots of problems concerning cross boundary visits! There were always problems concerning holiday relief, the report states that the Tardebigge Nurse has done the relief work on another area as well as her own patch, but no-one was anxious to do the relief work on the Tardebigge area!!!

The Secretary drew to the Committee's attention that according to the local paper a Superintendent from the Worcester County Nursing had called a meeting in the Bromsgrove area of all local nursing associations to explain to them a very complicated Rushcliffe Report. Why was Tardebigge not invited? Also, someone had reported to Worcester that Nurse had attended a case outside her own district, <u>she must never do this</u>, unless the Committee of both Associations agree. Will the Honourary Secretary please write to the County Secretary and state that it is quite impossible to call two Committees together at a moments notice to decide whether Nurse may attend an urgent maternity case....

The A.G.M. 1946.

The time has come when we must regretfully give Nurse notice, she already knew the condition but we must put it on an official footing.

It was proposed that an open letter be printed telling subscribers which district they will come under.

You will all know that Tardebigge District Nursing Association is to be dissolved. The only thing that can soften the blow of this change is the fact that the National Health Service will come into force and all voluntary organisations will be finished. I think that we can feel that we are one of the first victims of the scheme.

The business concluded with a presentation to nurse, a shopping bag and a cheque for £25.00 The funds were divided between Redditch, Headless Cross, Hanbury and Bromsgrove, Hanbury receiving a higher proportion as their district have to buy a car to enable their nurse to do Bentley.

The decision was that this minute book be deposited at the Vicarage to be kept with other Parish Documents.

AUTHOR'S COMMENT

IT APPEARS TO HAVE STRAYED FROM THE FOLD AND AFTER ALL THESE YEARS THE BATTLE IS STILL RAGING.

CHAPTER TEN

After the ball...

No one realised just how sad the future years would be when Ivor Miles, Earl of Plymouth died in 1943. This was the Earl that I had seen at our Christmas Parties.

Bad news always travels quickly. Notices appeared in the press. Big headlines hit you in the eye wherever you looked....

HEWELL GRANGE TO BE SOLD...............

THE BIRMINGHAM POST, SATURDAY, SEPT...

HEWELL GRANGE TO BE SOLD

Hewell Grange, the Worcestershire seat of the Earl of Plymouth, with the estate of 5,500 acres, to be sold. The estate has been in the possession of the family for 400 years. At one time it was much larger and included most of the Lickey Hills, now the chief of Birmingham's open spaces.

Lord Plymouth, who is twenty-one and succeeded his father in 1943, has sent an explanation to his farmer tenants. "The very large death duties which have to be paid," he writes, "make it inevitable that I should sell the estate. I am making every effort to ensure that it is sold as a whole, hoping in these circumstances that the tenants will be more likely to be left undisturbed."

Hewell lies midway between Bromsgrove and Redditch, and the estate stretches into the industrial quarter of Redditch. Throughout the war the Grange and its park have been used by the R.A.O.C. as an ammunition and armoured vehicle depot, and a large body of troops is still in possession.

Lord Plymouth has made St. Fagan's Castle, near Cardiff, his country home.

These postcards of St Fagan's Castle near Cardiff were posted by my sister Isobel to my parents.

It was the custom of the Earl and Countess of Plymouth to take some of their staff from Hewell Grange along with them when they were in residence at St. Fagan's.

Both cards bear 1d penny stamps (old money) dated 1921.

On the back is written...
Dear M & D.
Thankyou very much for your letter. Will write later. We are very busy getting cleared up after the visitors, the Prince (Prince of Wales) went this morning, hope you are getting on alright with the bedrooms and poultry farm.
With best love   I.A.W. (Isobel Alice Warner).

This card reads...
I could not get this in an envelope so I send it like this.....
Love I.A.W.

CHAPTER ELEVEN

The end of an era

Many changes have taken place in Tardebigge since 1928 when a little girl was taken on her first visit to Tardebigge Village Hall and became enthralled with the "pictures" (Bas Reliefs) on the walls inside the main hall.

During the sale of the Hewell Estate in 1945 the Village Hall was bought by Ralph Edwards Enterprises to be used as a country club. It became known as "The Tardebigge". Some years later it was sold to Ansell's Brewery and the name remained unchanged.

For two or three years it stood empty and neglected, perhaps it was haunted by the ghost of an English gentleman who many years ago had stated "No intoxicating liquor is allowed on these premises".

In 1946 Hewell Grange was sold to the Government and a new era began, so sad because Bromsgrove and Redditch were desperate for a maternity home, it became a H.M. Borstal Training Establishment for young men.

The exterior grounds and gardens remain unchanged and the property is open to the public every three years.

Whilst I was working on the research for my previous book I made an appointment to visit the Grange, I was longing to go there again but somehow I always managed to miss the "Open Days".

I had heard many conflicting reports so, at last, after what seemed almost a life time I was once more transported back to my first school party in 1929. I was treated like a V.I.P. by the Deputy Governor and staff and was able to retrace many steps and many memories.

The porter's lodges still remain on the old road which winds it's way up past the Village Hall over Tardebigge tunnel, through Tutnall and Finstall into Aston Fields and onto Bromsgrove. No longer can one quietly wander from the church down the little school lane which would take you to the Lodge at the entrance to Hewell Park, or meander across the Pleck which would lead you across the fields to the Village Hall, the same way that as school children we walked to our cookery classes. Plymouth House where the leggers drank their ale is now a nursing home.

In 1982 the hall once again changed hands and extensive alterations began and it is now known as "The Tardebigge" a licenced restaurant and bar.

I realised that it would be necessary to try and obtain some better photographs of "my pictures" and wondered if it would still be cold and

Tardebigge Church & School & Top Lock House
- A38 Bromsgrove Highway

dark inside. Maybe this time I could linger a little longer and maybe..............
I might be able to spend a few minutes and be alone with my memories and
maybe...who knows I could look at my beloved pictures again...I would be
able to stand and listen to the music and hear the applause from the
Christmas Panto's
Echoes of childrens laughter and chattering little voices. I would hear the
shouts from the cricket team on a warm summer evening, the crack of
bowls as they rolled down the bowling green.
Maybe...if I could spare the time to listen, I might hear the ghostly sounds
drifting across from the weaving room...well who knows?
All this was running through my head as I travelled along. I had arranged to
meet my eldest son Peter to take another lot of photographs. I had the
previous ones with me as proof of our visit and we knew access would be
easy, we had seen the lorries outside. We approached a workman and
explained the reason for our visit..."Mmm, You're too late that wall was
demolished a week ago". Frozen to the spot I said, "But what about the
sculptures on the wall?" The answer was devastating..."Oh, they're all
smashed up in the rubble somewhere (so matter of factish).
I stood there speechless, my first thought was to scramble and scrape
amongst the high pile of rubble to see if I could piece together any

fragments I could find, but alas it was useless...

For with "my pictures" not only did we lose a little bit of the history of Tardebigge...with them also went....just a tiny little fragment of the history of England...

In June 1977 Tardebigge Church held its Bi-Centenary. An exhibition of local crafts was on show including Basketry, poetry and weaving.

A history of the canal with tools of the trade was also on show, also included were extracts by the late George Bates with his British Empire Medal.

I thoroughly enjoyed the play which was acted by the local band of "mummers", the theme of which was the "Lock Keeper and his daughters". Some of the characters were dressed in old fashioned smocks and mop caps and brandished wooden hay rakes and pitch forks. I think they had come up from the Halfway House just for the occasion...

The present Earl of Plymouth was present at this occasion.

It was the end of an era...

TARDEBIGGE VILLAGE HALL
Drawing by Janette Hill from an original drawing by David Hill